ANALYTIC
GEOMETRY $\sqrt{\text{and } an \text{ introduction } to}$
 CALCULUS

PRENTICE-HALL, Inc.

Englewood Cliffs, N. J.

ANALYTIC
GEOMETRY

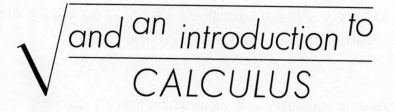

$\sqrt{\text{and } ^{an} \text{ introduction } ^{to}}$

CALCULUS

A. CLYDE SCHOCK

Head, Department of Mathematics
Central High School, Philadelphia

BERNARD S. WARSHAW

Instructor of Mathematics
Central High School, Philadelphia

ANALYTIC GEOMETRY AND AN INTRODUCTION TO CALCULUS
A. Clyde Schock, Bernard S. Warshaw

LIBRARY OF CONGRESS CATALOG CARD NO. 60-6639

Printed in the United States of America

03449

PREFACE

Analytic Geometry and an Introduction to Calculus contains material for a one-semester course for students taking a complete program of mathematics.

In recent years, there has been a growing tendency to give college freshmen a course in analytic geometry and the calculus. This text is written to help bridge the gap between the mathematics usually taught in the senior year of high school and this mathematics of the freshman year of college.

This textbook is the product of a number of years of actual classroom experience and experimentation. Indeed, so favorable has been the pupil response, particularly from those who were in their first year of college, and so numerous the requests for copies of the mimeographed manuscript, that the authors are convinced that the presentation of this material in textbook form will be of service to other students and teachers.

The authors have attempted to make certain that both the development and the content of the text are mathematically correct without involving rigor that is beyond the mathematical maturity of the students using the text.

The authors take this opportunity to express their indebtedness to the many students who have worked with the mimeographed version and who have thus served as an inspiration for the creation of this text.

They also wish to acknowledge the advice and assistance of Willette M. Petty, Fremont High School, Oakland, California, and John J. Kinsella, School of Education, New York University.

CONTENTS

1

FUNCTIONS

1-1 Introduction

If two variables, x and y, are so related that for each value of x there corresponds one value of y, then y is said to be a *function* of x.

For example, if $y = 3x - 2$, then for each value of x, there is a corresponding value of y, as follows:

If $x = 2$, then $y = 4$, and
if $x = 0$, then $y = -2$, and
if $x = \frac{2}{3}$, then $y = 0$, etc.

In this case, x is called the *independent variable* and y is called the *dependent variable*, since the value of y depends upon the value of x, chosen independently.

The role of the variables as dependent and independent can be interchanged by solving the given equation for x in terms of y.

For example, if $\qquad y = 3x - 2,$
then $\qquad\qquad 3x = y + 2,$
and $\qquad\qquad x = \frac{1}{3}y + \frac{2}{3}.$

Here, y is the independent variable, x is the dependent variable, and x is a function of y.

1

Variables can be represented by other letters than x and y. Thus, in the formula

$$PV = k,$$

solving for P gives

$$P = \frac{k}{V},$$

where V is the independent variable and P the dependent variable; while solving for V gives

$$V = \frac{k}{P},$$

where P is the independent variable and V the dependent variable.

However, in this text it is assumed that, in all equations which involve x and y, x is the independent variable and y is the dependent variable.

1-2 Notations for Functions

The notations $y = f(x)$, $y = \phi(x)$, $y = g(x)$, etc., are used to denote that y is a function of x. These are read, "y equals f of x, y equals phi of x and y equals g of x," respectively. The same symbol is always used in a given discussion to mean the same functional relation.

Further, if a is any value of x, then

$f(a)$ represents the value of $f(x)$ at $x = a$.

For example, if

$$y = f(x) = 3x - 2,$$

then
$$f(2) = 3(2) - 2 = 6 - 2 = 4,$$
$$f(0) = 3(0) - 2 = 0 - 2 = -2,$$
$$f(-4) = 3(-4) - 2 = -12 - 2 = -14,$$
$$f(a - 2) = 3(a - 2) - 2 = 3a - 6 - 2 = 3a - 8.$$

Also, if $g(x) = 3x^2 - 2x - 4,$

then
$$g(0) = 3(0) - 2(0) - 4 = 0 - 0 - 4 = -4,$$
$$g(1) = 3(1) - 2(1) - 4 = 3 - 2 - 4 = -3,$$
$$g(4) = 3(16) - 2(4) - 4 = 48 - 8 - 4 = 36.$$

1-3 Domain and Range

The set of all real values of the independent variable x, for which real values of $f(x)$ can be obtained is called the *domain of definition,* or just the *domain* of the function. The corresponding set of values of $f(x)$ is called the *range* of the function.

In the two examples which are given above, the domain is the set of real numbers, and the range is also the set of real numbers. However, in the function

$$y = f(x) = \frac{2x + 1}{x - 1},$$

$$f(1) = \frac{2 + 1}{1 - 1} = \frac{3}{0}.$$

Since division by 0 is impossible, there is no value for $f(x)$ at $x = 1$. Accordingly, the domain of this function is the set of real numbers, except 1.

In order to find the range of this function, solve the equation

$$y = \frac{2x + 1}{x - 1} \text{ for } x.$$

Then, $$xy - y = 2x + 1$$
and $$xy - 2x = y + 1.$$

Therefore, $$x = \frac{y + 1}{y - 2}.$$

Accordingly, the range of the function is the set of real numbers, except 2.

Further, in order that y may be a real number in the function $y = f(x) = \sqrt{9 - x^2}$, x must be less than or equal to 3 or greater than or equal to -3.

This fact may be written $-3 \leq x \leq 3$.

The above relation can also be written $|x| \leq 3$, where the symbol $|x|$ is read "the absolute value of x."

By definition, the *absolute value* of zero or a positive number is the same as the number itself, while the absolute value of a negative number is this number with its sign changed.

Thus, $|3| = 3$, $|0| = 0$ and $|-3| = -(-3) = 3$.

Accordingly, the range of $f(x) = \sqrt{9 - x^2}$ is the set of real numbers $|x| \leq 3$.

E X E R C I S E S

1. If $f(x) = x - 3$, find:

$f(0)$; $f(1)$; $f(5)$;

$f(-2)$; $f(x - 1)$.

2. If $f(x) = 4x - 2$, find:

$f(1)$; $f(-2)$; $f(0)$;

$f(\frac{3}{2})$; $f(2a - 1)$.

3. If $F(x) = 4x^2 + 5$, find:

$F(2)$; $F(-1)$; $F(\sqrt{2})$;

$F(0)$; $F(\frac{1}{2})$.

4. If $g(x) = 3x^2 - 2x + 1$, find:

$g(0)$; $g(4)$; $g(-2)$;

$g(\frac{1}{3})$; $g(x + h)$.

5. If $f(x) = \dfrac{x + 1}{x - 1}$, find:

$f(0)$; $f(3)$; $f(-5)$;

$f(\frac{1}{2})$; $f\left(\dfrac{1}{x}\right)$.

6. If $G(x) = \sqrt{x^2 - 4}$, find:

$G(2)$; $G(-2)$; $G(-5)$;

$G(3)$; $G(\frac{5}{2})$.

7. If $F(\theta) = \sin 2\theta + \cos \theta$, where θ is expressed in radians, find:

$F(0)$; $F\left(\dfrac{\pi}{2}\right)$; $F\left(\dfrac{\pi}{4}\right)$;

$F(\pi)$; $F\left(\dfrac{3\pi}{2}\right)$.

8. What is the domain and the range of the following functions?

$y = f(x) = x - 2$;
$y = f(x) = 2x + 1$;
$y = f(x) = 3x - 5$;

$y = f(x) = \dfrac{x + 1}{x - 2}$.

9. What is the domain and the range of the following functions?

$y = f(x) = x^2 + 1$;

$y = f(x) = \dfrac{1}{1 + \sqrt{x}}$;

$y = f(x) = \dfrac{x}{x - 1}$;

$y = f(x) = \sqrt{x^2 - 16}$.

10. What is the domain of the following functions?

$$f(x) = \frac{1}{(x - 2)(x + 2)};$$

$$G(t) = \sqrt{t^2 - 4};$$

$$\phi(x) = \sqrt{10 - x^2};$$

$$F(x) = \frac{1}{x(x - 2)}.$$

11. What is the domain of the following functions?

$$F(x) = \sqrt{(x - 5)(3 - x)};$$

$$\phi(x) = \frac{1}{2x(x + 1)};$$

$$G(x) = \sqrt{\frac{x + 1}{x}};$$

$$g(x) = \frac{x + 2}{\sqrt{x^2 - 2}}.$$

12. If $f(x) = \dfrac{1}{x}$ and $g(x) = \dfrac{1 - x}{x}$, find:

$f[g(x)];$ $g[f(x)];$

$f[f(x)];$ $g[g(x)].$

2

COORDINATES AND GRAPHS

2-1 Introduction

Analytic geometry may be defined as the study of geometric figures by algebraic methods. A geometric figure can be analyzed by means of the points which it contains. Accordingly, in analytic geometry there is a method of associating each point of space with a set of numbers and of studying the relations among these sets of numbers by the methods of algebra.

Plane analytic geometry, which is considered in this text, is the study of the algebra of geometric configurations in a plane.

2-2 Rectangular Coordinates

A two-dimensional space is a space in which two measurements are needed to locate any point with respect to an arbitrarily chosen point. The following figure (Fig. 2-1) illustrates the fact that a plane is a two-dimensional space and not a one-dimensional space.

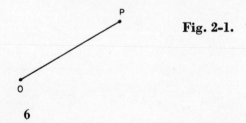

Fig. 2-1.

Take O as the arbitrarily chosen point on the plane of this page and let P be any other point in the page. From Fig. 2-1, it is apparent that the distance OP does not determine the location of point P, since the line segment OP can be rotated around O and hence can locate an infinity of points which are at the distance OP from O.

In order to locate P uniquely on a plane with respect to O it is necessary to employ two measurements, as follows:

Let O (Fig. 2-2) be the arbitrarily chosen point and P the point to be located. Through O draw any line OX, and draw OY perpendicular to OX at O.

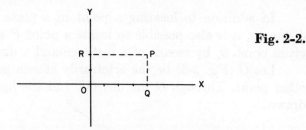

Fig. 2-2.

Draw RP parallel to OX and QP parallel to OY.

Thus the point P is located uniquely by counting 4 units to the right of OY and 2 units up from OX.

By general agreement, measurements to the right of OY are considered positive and measurements to the left of OY are considered negative; while measurements up from OX are considered positive and measurements down from OX are considered negative.

The arbitrarily chosen point is called the *origin* and the lines OX and OY are called the *coordinate axes*, with OX the x-axis and OY the y-axis. The distance OQ is the first number stated and is called the *abscissa* of the point P, and the distance QP is the second number stated and is called the *ordinate* of the point P. These two numbers are called the *coordinates* of the point and are written $P(4,2)$.

If P is a variable point (i.e., a moving point), its coordinates are x and y and written $P(x, y)$, where the value of x is the abscissa and the value of y is the ordinate of the point P.

This system of coordinates is called the system of *rectangular Cartesian coordinates* (rectangular because the axes are at right angles to each other, and Cartesian in honor of Rene Descartes, who first introduced the methods of analytic geometry).

Thus, it is seen that for each point in a given plane there is one pair of coordinates.

Let $y = f(x)$, and select values for the independent variable x. Corresponding to each value of x, there is a value for the dependent variable y. Each pair of values for x and y gives a point on the plane. Since any desired number of such points can be found, it is seen that any algebraic equation in x and y can be analyzed geometrically. Further, any algebraic equation in not more than two variables represents a geometrical figure in two-dimensional space, i.e., in a plane.

2-3 Polar Coordinates

In addition to locating a point in a plane by means of two distances, it is also possible to locate a point P with reference to a given point O, by means of a distance and a direction, as follows:

Let O (Fig. 2-3) be the arbitrarily chosen point and P be any other point. Through O the line OR and the line segment OP are drawn.

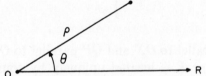

Fig. 2-3.

Then P is located uniquely on the plane by the angle ROP, designated θ (read "theta") and by the length of the line segment OP, designated ρ (read "rho"). Such a system of coordinates is called a system of *polar coordinates*. A further discussion of polar coordinates is to be found in Chapter 6.

2-4 Other Spaces

A one-dimensional space is a space in which one measurement is needed to locate a point P with respect to an arbitrarily chosen point O. Accordingly, a straight line is a one-dimensional space.

For example, let AB (Fig. 2-4) be a straight line of indefinite length, with O the arbitrarily chosen point, called the *origin*. Also, let P_1 and P_2 be two points on the line AB.

$$\text{A} \xleftrightarrow{\quad P_2 \quad\quad O \quad\quad P_1 \quad} \text{B}$$ **Fig. 2-4.**

Further, let it be agreed that distances to the right of O be considered positive and distances to the left of O be considered negative. From Fig. 2-4, it is seen that $OP_1 = 3$ and $OP_2 = -2$.

Therefore, in general, only one coordinate is needed to locate a particular point on a line. Hence, an equation in at most one variable, x, represents a set of points on the one dimensional line, AB.

A three-dimensional space is a space in which three measurements are needed to locate a point with respect to an arbitrarily chosen point. In this space, the three coordinates x, y, and z are needed to locate the point $P(x,y,z)$. Hence, an algebraic equation in at most three variables, x, y, and z, represents a geometric configuration in a three-dimensional space.

Likewise, an algebraic equation in at most four variables, x, y, z, and t, represents a configuration in four-dimensional space. And, in general, an algebraic equation in at most n variables represents a configuration in n-dimensional space.

2-5 Plotting Points

For the purpose of plotting points on a given plane, the coordinate axes are calibrated with a convenient unit of length, making the unit fit the particular problem under consideration. *Since the purpose of the graph is to illustrate the problem and to facilitate its analysis, all graphs should be sketched freehand and without the use of graph paper, but always should be drawn neatly.*

EXAMPLE. Plot the points:

$A(5,3)$;
$B(7,0)$;
$C(0,-5)$;
$D(-4,-4)$;
$E(-3,5)$.

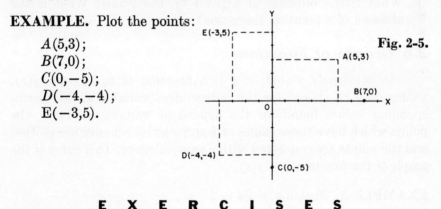

Fig. 2-5.

E X E R C I S E S

1. Plot the points:

$P_1(3,2)$;	$P_6(2,2)$;
$P_2(-4,0)$;	$P_7(-4,-7)$;
$P_3(0,1)$;	$P_8(-6,5)$;
$P_4(1,-5)$;	$P_9(-3,8)$;
$P_5(-5,2)$;	$P_{10}(-7,-7)$.

2. Find the coordinates of each of the lettered points in Fig. 2-6.

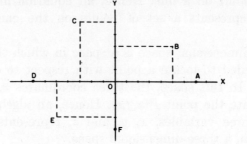

Fig. 2-6.

3. Plot the points:

$A(7,3)$;	$D(-5,3)$;
$B(0,3)$;	$E(6,-2)$;
$C(-2,3)$;	$F(-7,0)$.

4. Give the coordinates of any four points that lie on a circle whose center is at the origin and whose radius is 5.

5. Plot the points:

$A(3,5)$;	$C(-4,-2)$;
$B(3,-2)$;	$D(-4,5)$.

What kind of a figure is $ABCD$?

6. What is the ordinate of a point on the x-axis? What is the abscissa of a point on the y-axis?

2-6 *Graphs of Functions*

As previously stated, if y is a function of x, i.e., $y = f(x)$, values may be chosen for the independent variable x, and corresponding values found for the dependent variable y. Then, the points which have these values of x and y as coordinates are plotted and the points are connected with a smooth curve. This curve is the graph of the function $y = f(x)$.

EXAMPLE 1. Sketch $y = 2x - 3$.

First, prepare a table of corresponding values of x and y, as follows:

x	0	-1	2	3	$\frac{3}{2}$
y	-3	-5	1	3	0

Plot these points and connect them with a smooth curve, as in

Fig. 2-7. All the five points found in this example *seem* to lie on the same straight line. In the next chapter (Chapter 3), it will be proved that these points actually *do* lie on the same straight line.

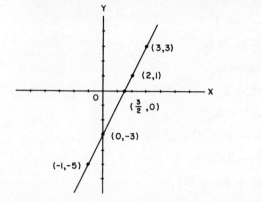

Fig. 2-7.

In the equation $y = 2x - 3$, when $x = 0$, then $y = -3$. This value of y which corresponds to the value of $x = 0$ is called the *y-intercept* of the curve. Similarly, the value of x, which corresponds to the value of $y = 0$, is called the *x-intercept* of the curve. It is seen from the figure that the y-intercept is the point where the curve crosses the y-axis and the x-intercept is the point where the curve crosses the x-axis.

EXAMPLE 2. Sketch $y = x^2 - 4x + 3$.

Prepare the table of corresponding values of x and y:

x	0	1	2	3	4
y	3	0	-1	0	3

Plot these points and connect them with a smooth curve, as in Fig. 2-8.

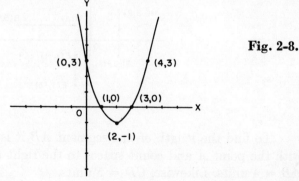

Fig. 2-8.

E X E R C I S E S

Sketch the graphs of the following equations:

1. $y = 3x - 2$.
2. $y = -x + 1$.
3. $y = -2x + 5$.
4. $y = 5x - 3$.
5. $y = x^2 - 2$.
6. $y = 2x^2 - 5$.
7. $y = 3 - x^2$.
8. $y = 2 - 3x^2$.
9. $y = x^2 + 4x + 5$.
10. $y = 2x^2 - 8x + 5$.
11. $y = 2 + 2x - x^2$.
12. $x^2 + y^2 = 25$. (Solve for $y = \pm\sqrt{25 - x^2}$.)

2-7 Length of Line Segments Parallel to an Axis

If a line segment is parallel to the x-axis, it is considered positive if it is measured to the right, and negative if it is measured to the left. Similarly, if a line segment is parallel to the y-axis, it is considered positive if it is measured upward and negative if it is measured downward.

For example, line segments AB and EF (Fig. 2-9) are considered positive and line segments DC and HG are considered negative.

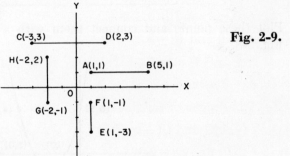

Fig. 2-9.

To find the length of line segment AB it is necessary to start with the point A and count spaces to the right to point B. Hence, $AB = 4$ units. Likewise, $CD = 5$ units.

To find the length of EF, start with E and count upward to F. Hence, $EF = 2$. Likewise, $GH = 3$.

Further, to find the length of BA, start with B and count to the left to A. Hence $BA = -4$. Likewise, $FE = -2$.

In general, since the points $P_1(x_1,y_1)$ and $P_2(x_2,y_1)$ have the same ordinates (Fig. 2-10), the line segment P_1P_2 is parallel to the x-axis and its length equals the difference of the abscissas of the points P_1 and P_2. Therefore,

$$P_1P_2 = x_2 - x_1$$

and
$$P_2P_1 = x_1 - x_2.$$

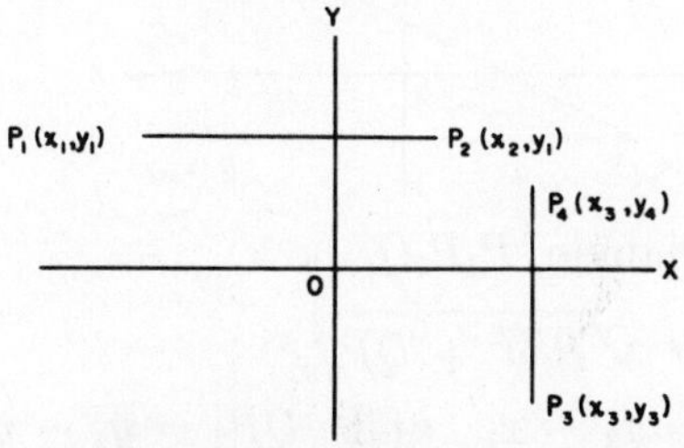

Fig. 2-10.

Likewise, since the points $P_3(x_3,y_3)$ and $P_4(x_3,y_4)$ have the same abscissas, the line segment P_3P_4 is parallel to the y-axis. Therefore,

$$P_3P_4 = y_4 - y_3$$

and
$$P_4P_3 = y_3 - y_4.$$

E X E R C I S E S

Find the length of the line segment AB for each of the following pairs of points:

1. $A(3,7)$ and $B(3,2)$.

2. $A(0,-4)$ and $B(0,3)$.

3. $A(5,0)$ and $B(-3,0)$.

4. $A(-3,-1)$ and $B(-3,-7)$.

5. $A(-1,4)$ and $B(7,4)$.

Find the length of the line segment PQ for:

6. $P(-1,7)$ and $Q(-1,-1)$.

7. $P(5,0)$ and $Q(-2,0)$.

8. $P(-2,-5)$ and $Q(-2,3)$.

9. $P(a,b)$ and $Q(a,0)$.

10. $P(7,-3)$ and $Q(-2,-3)$.

2-8 Length of Line Segments Not Parallel to an Axis

If a line segment is not parallel to either axis, its length is always considered to be positive. The formula for the length of such a line segment is derived as follows:

Let $P_1(x_1,y_1)$ and $P_2(x_2,y_2)$ be the endpoints of the given line segment P_1P_2. Draw P_1Q parallel to the x-axis and QP_2 parallel to the y-axis (Fig. 2-11), locating the point $Q(x_2,y_1)$.

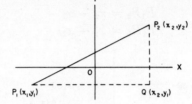

Fig. 2-11.

In the right triangle, P_1P_2Q,
$$P_1P_2 = \sqrt{\overline{P_1Q}^2 + \overline{QP_2}^2}.$$
Since $\qquad P_1Q = x_2 - x_1 \quad \text{and} \quad QP_2 = y_2 - y_1,$

then, $\qquad d = P_1P_2 = \sqrt{(x_2 - x_1)^2 + (y_2 - y_1)^2}.$

Since $(x_2 - x_1)^2 = (x_1 - x_2)^2$ and $(y_2 - y_1)^2 = (y_1 - y_2)^2$, the formula remains the same if the subscripts are interchanged. Thus it makes no difference which point is designated by P_1.

This formula is not to be used with lines that are parallel to an axis, since then the directional effect is lost.

EXAMPLE 1. Find the length of the line segment joining the points $P_1(-2,5)$ and $P_2(3,-7)$.
$$d = P_1P_2 = \sqrt{(-2 - 3)^2 + (5 + 7)^2}$$
$$= \sqrt{25 + 144} = \sqrt{169} = 13.$$

EXAMPLE 2. Show that the points $A(-2,7)$, $B(4,1)$, and $C(6,9)$ are the vertices of an isosceles triangle.

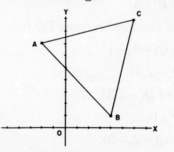

Fig. 2-12.

$$AB = \sqrt{(-2-4)^2 + (7-1)^2} = \sqrt{36+36} = \sqrt{72} = 6\sqrt{2},$$
$$BC = \sqrt{(4-6)^2 + (1-9)^2} = \sqrt{4+64} = \sqrt{68} = 2\sqrt{17},$$
$$CA = \sqrt{(6+2)^2 + (9-7)^2} = \sqrt{64+4} = \sqrt{68} = 2\sqrt{17}.$$

Since $BC = CA$, the triangle is isosceles.

E X E R C I S E S

Find the distances between the following pairs of points:

1. $(7,5)$ and $(3,2)$.

2. $(5,8)$ and $(0,-4)$.

3. $(-3,-6)$ and $(1,-3)$.

4. $(2,4)$ and $(-4,2)$.

5. $(7,-3)$ and $(-1,5)$.

6. $(-3,-2)$ and $(2,0)$.

7. $(3,-4)$ and $(-3,4)$.

8. $(3,-5)$ and $(9,1)$.

9. $(0,0)$ and $(-4,3)$.

10. $(1,3)$ and $(3,-5)$.

11. $(3,-2)$ and $(-5,13)$.

12. $(\frac{1}{2},-\frac{5}{2})$ and $(\frac{7}{2},\frac{3}{2})$.

13. $(3a,6b)$ and $(-2a,b)$.

14. Find the lengths of the sides of the triangle whose vertices are $(2,7)$, $(-4,1)$, and $(4,-3)$.

15. Show that the origin is the center of the circle passing through the points $(4,-3)$, $(0,5)$, and $(-3,-4)$.

16. Show that the points $(3,4)$, $(-5,-2)$, and $(8,-11)$ are the vertices of an isosceles triangle.

17. Prove that the points $(3,-3)$, $(5,3)$, $(2,6)$, and $(0,0)$ are the vertices of a parallelogram.

18. Show that the points $(-3,7)$, $(-1,-5)$, and $(4,2)$ are the vertices of a right triangle.

19. Show that the points $(4,6)$, $(-4,2)$, and $(0,-2)$ are the vertices of an isosceles triangle.

20. Show that the points $(1,-5)$, $(-2,6)$, and $(-4,-4)$ are the vertices of a right triangle.

21. Identify the triangle whose vertices are $(5,11)$, $(-7,6)$, and $(-2,-6)$.

22. Identify the triangle whose vertices are $(3,-2)$, $(-1,-5)$, and $(6,-6)$.

23. If the vertices of a right triangle- are $A(5,k)$, $B(6,-6)$, and $C(2,-3)$ and the vertex of the right angle is at C, find the value of k.

2-9 *Midpoint of a Line Segment*

Let $M(x_0,y_0)$ be the midpoint of the line segment P_1P_2, where the coordinates of P_1 are (x_1,y_1) and the coordinates of P_2 are (x_2,y_2), as in Fig. 2-13.

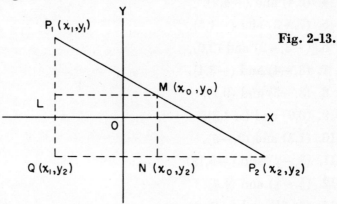

Fig. 2-13.

Draw QP_2 parallel to the x-axis and QP_1 and NM parallel to the y-axis.

Then the coordinates of Q are (x_1, y_2) and the coordinates of N are (x_0,y_2).

Since the line MN which bisects P_1P_2 and is parallel to QP_1 must bisect the line QP_2,

then $$QN = NP_2.$$

Therefore, $$x_0 - x_1 = x_2 - x_0,$$
$$2x_0 = x_1 + x_2,$$

and $$x_0 = \frac{x_1 + x_2}{2}.$$

In a similar manner, by drawing LM parallel to the x-axis, it is possible to prove that

$$y_0 = \frac{y_1 + y_2}{2}.$$

EXAMPLE 1. Find the coordinates of the midpoint of the line segment whose endpoints are $(3, -1)$ and $(-5, 3)$.

Since
$$x_0 = \frac{3 - 5}{2} = \frac{-2}{2} = -1$$

and
$$y_0 = \frac{-1 + 3}{2} = \frac{2}{2} = 1,$$

the coordinates of the midpoint are $(-1, 1)$.

EXAMPLE 2. Prove analytically that the diagonals of a parallelogram bisect each other.

Place the given parallelogram on a system of coordinates so that one of its vertices falls on the origin and one of its sides falls along the positive direction of the x-axis, as in Fig. 2-14.

Let the length of the side along the x-axis be a. Then two of the vertices of the parallelogram are the points $O(0,0)$ and $A(a,0)$. Further, let the coordinates of vertex B, which is the vertex opposite to A, be (b,c). Then the coordinates of the fourth vertex C are $(a + b, c)$, since
$$DC = DB + BC$$
$$= DB + OA$$
$$= b + a = a + b.$$

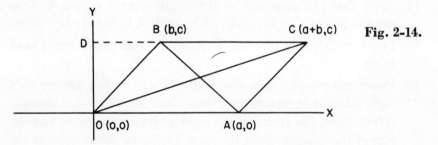

Fig. 2-14.

By the midpoint formulas, the coordinates of the midpoint of the diagonal OC are $\left(\dfrac{a + b}{2}, \dfrac{c}{2}\right)$, and the coordinates of the midpoint of the diagonal AB are $\left(\dfrac{a + b}{2}, \dfrac{c}{2}\right)$.

Since the two straight lines OC and AB can intersect in not more than one point, then the point $\left(\dfrac{a + b}{2}, \dfrac{c}{2}\right)$ is the common midpoint of both lines.

Therefore, the diagonals OC and AB bisect each other.

Find the coordinates of the midpoint of the line segment AB in the following:

1. $A(3,3); B(9,1).$
2. $A(3,-7); B(-5,-3).$
3. $A(-2,-8); B(-4,0).$
4. $A(4,-7); B(-2,1).$
5. $A(-5,5); B(-2,-2).$
6. $A(7,0); B(4,2).$
7. $A(-1,-9); B(-3,-5).$
8. $A(-8,3); B(-2,-3).$
9. $A(11,9); B(1,5).$
10. $A(0,a); B(b,0).$
11. $A(7,11); B(-2,8).$
12. $A(8,-4); B(-3,5).$

13. Find the midpoints of the sides of the triangle whose vertices are the points $(-3,6)$, $(3,2)$, and $(5,8)$.

14. Find the lengths of the medians of the triangle whose vertices are given in Exercise 13.

15. Find the center and the radius of the circle, one of whose diameters is the line segment with the endpoints $(-3,8)$ and $(3,0)$.

16. The point $(-2,2)$ is the midpoint of a line segment, one of whose endpoints is at $(5,7)$. Find the coordinates of the other endpoint of the segment.

17. Show that the diagonals of the parallelogram, whose vertices are the points $(5,-2)$, $(7,4)$, $(4,7)$, and $(2,1)$ bisect each other.

18. Prove analytically that the diagonals of a rectangle bisect each other.

19. Prove analytically that the midpoint of the hypotenuse of a right triangle is equidistant from the vertices of the triangle. [*Hint:* Place the vertex of the right angle on the origin and the legs of the triangle along the axes. Then, the coordinates of the vertices are $(0,0)$, $(a,0)$, and $(0,b)$.]

20. Prove analytically that the line connecting the midpoints of any two sides of a triangle is equal to one-half the third side. [*Hint:* Place one vertex of the triangle at the origin and the base along the positive direction of the x-axis. Then, the coordinates of the vertices are $(0,0)$, $(a,0)$, and (b,c).]

3

THE STRAIGHT LINE

3-1 Inclination and Slope

The *angle of inclination*, α (read "alpha") of a straight line is the angle which the line makes with the positive direction of the x-axis, or with a line parallel to the x-axis, measured in a counter-clockwise direction.

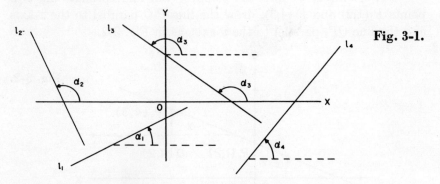

Fig. 3-1.

Thus, from Fig. 3-1, it is seen that

$$0 \leq \alpha < \pi \quad \text{or} \quad 0° \leq \alpha < 180°.$$

(Note that if an angle has no unit designation it is assumed that the angle is measured in radians.)

19

It is immaterial which point is chosen as the point from which the positive direction of the x-axis is drawn, since, if parallel lines are cut by a transversal, the corresponding angles are equal, as is seen in the case of line l_3.

Again, the quadrant in which the line is drawn does not determine whether the angle α is acute or obtuse, since α_1 and α_4 are acute and α_2 and α_3 are obtuse.

It is often convenient to measure the direction of a line by the tangent of its angle of inclination which is called its *slope, m.*

Thus, $$m = \tan \alpha.$$

Since the tangent of an acute angle is positive and the tangent of an obtuse angle is negative, then m_1, the slope of line l_1, and m_4, the slope of line l_4, (Fig. 3-1) are positive, while m_2 and m_3 are negative.

The sign of the slope of any line can be determined very easily by employing the following rule:

*If the line **goes upward,** as the point moves along the line from **left to right,** the slope is **positive;** while if the line goes **downward,** as the point moves along the line from **left to right,** the slope is **negative.***

3-2 Slope of a Line Through Two Points

The slope of a line can be found from the coordinates of any two points which lie on the line.

For example, to find the slope of the line through the two points $P_1(1,2)$ and $P_2(4,3)$, draw the line P_1Q parallel to the x-axis and the line QP_2 parallel to the y-axis, as in Fig. 3-2.

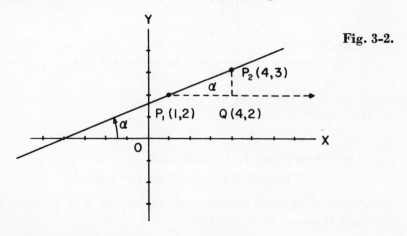

Fig. 3-2.

Now, $$\tan \alpha = \frac{QP_2}{P_1Q} = \frac{3-2}{4-1} = \frac{1}{3}.$$

Further, if $P_3(-2,-4)$ and $P_4(-6,1)$ are two points on line l_2 (Fig. 3-3), then the slope of line l_2 is $\dfrac{QP_4}{QP_3}.$

Then, $$m_2 = \frac{1+4}{-6+2} = -\frac{5}{4}.$$

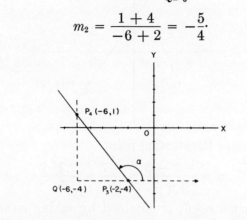

Fig. 3-3.

In general, if $P_1(x_1,y_1)$ and $P_2(x_2,y_2)$ are two points on the line l (Fig. 3-4), the slope of the line is,

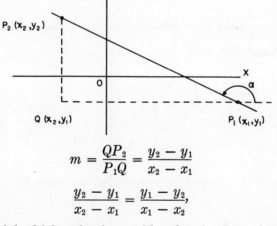

Fig. 3-4.

$$m = \frac{QP_2}{P_1Q} = \frac{y_2 - y_1}{x_2 - x_1}$$

Since $$\frac{y_2 - y_1}{x_2 - x_1} = \frac{y_1 - y_2}{x_1 - x_2},$$

it is immaterial which point is considered to be P_1 and which point P_2. However, it is essential to be consistent in a particular problem.

EXAMPLE 1. Find the slope of the line which passes through the points $P_1(3,-2)$ and $P_2(-2,5)$.

In Fig. 3-5, take P_1 as the starting point, then

$$m = \frac{5-(-2)}{-2-3} = \frac{7}{-5} = -\frac{7}{5}.$$

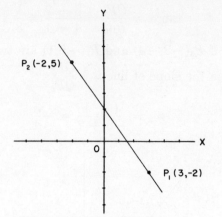

Fig. 3-5.

If P_2 is taken as the starting point,

$$m = \frac{-2 - 5}{3 + 2} = \frac{-7}{5} = -\frac{7}{5}.$$

Thus, the same result is obtained by taking either P_1 or P_2 as the starting point for computing the slope of the line.

EXAMPLE 2. Through the point $P(-1,2)$ draw the line whose slope is $-\frac{3}{2}$.

Since $-\frac{3}{2}$ may be considered as $\frac{3}{-2}$, then, as in Fig. 3-6, take $P_1Q = -2$ and $QP_2 = 3$.

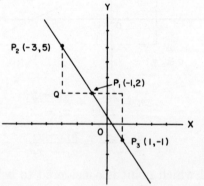

Fig. 3-6.

Then, by counting 2 units to the left from P_1 and 3 units up, the coordinates of P_2 are found to be $(-3,5)$ and the line drawn through P_1 and P_2 is the required line.

This construction may also be made as follows:

Since $-\frac{3}{2}$ may be considered as $\frac{-3}{2}$, then count 2 units to the right of P_1 and 3 units down to locate the point P_3, whose coordinates are found to be $(1,-1)$, as in Fig. 3-6. Then connect the two points P_1 and either P_2 or P_3 for the required line.

If the line is parallel to the x-axis, $m = 0$, since $\tan 0 = 0$. However, if the line is parallel to the y-axis, the slope has no value, since there is no tangent of $\frac{\pi}{2}$ (i.e., 90°). For convenience, it is sometimes said that the tangent of $\frac{\pi}{2}$ is ∞, which is read "infinity." Accordingly, the slope of a line parallel to the y-axis is said to be infinite, although, actually, there is no definite value for such a slope.

E X E R C I S E S

Find the slopes of the lines which pass through the following pairs of points:

1. $(3,-1)$ and $(5,-4)$.

2. $(-4,2)$ and $(3,5)$.

3. $(-5,3)$ and $(0,2)$.

4. $(0,0)$ and $(-4,3)$.

5. $(-3,3)$ and $(5,3)$.

6. $(7,-3)$ and $(3,5)$.

Draw the following straight lines:

7. Through $(3,2)$ with slope 2.

8. Through $(-4,3)$ with slope -1.

9. Through $(2,-3)$ with slope $\frac{1}{2}$.

10. Through $(4,-3)$ with slope $-\frac{2}{3}$.

11. Through $(0,0)$ with slope -2.

12. Through $(-2,5)$ with slope 0.

13. Through $(4,-2)$ with inclination $\frac{3\pi}{4}$.

14. Through $(-5,-1)$ with inclination $\frac{\pi}{4}$.

15. Show that the points $(2,6)$, $(-8,1)$, and $(-2,4)$ lie on the same straight line.

3-3 Standard Forms of the Equation of a Straight Line

The equation of a straight line is a relation between x and y which is satisfied by the coordinates of every point on the line. Since a straight line is determined either by two points or by a point and a direction, a number of standard forms of the equation of the straight line can be derived by the use of these conditions. Accordingly, the following standard forms of the equation of a straight line are considered:

(a) the point-slope form,
(b) the slope-intercept form,
(c) line through the origin,
(d) line parallel to an axis.

3-4 Point-Slope Form

Since a straight line is determined if a point on the line and the direction of the line are given, it is possible to employ these data to derive an equation for the line.

Let $P_1(x_1,y_1)$ be the given point through which the line passes and m the slope of the line. Further, let $P(x,y)$ be a point which moves along the line (Fig. 3-7).

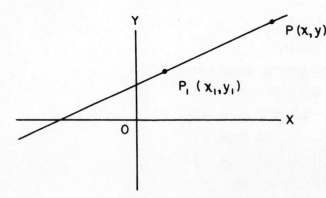

Fig. 3-7.

Since P and P_1 are two points on the line,

$$m = \frac{y - y_1}{x - x_1},$$

or
$$y - y_1 = m(x - x_1).$$

This is called the *point-slope* form of the equation of the straight line.

EXAMPLE 1. Find the equation of the straight line which passes through the point $(6, -4)$ and whose slope is $-\frac{1}{3}$.

By substitution, $\qquad y - (-4) = -\frac{1}{3}(x - 6),$

and $\qquad\qquad\qquad 3y + 12 = -x + 6,$

or $\qquad\qquad\qquad x + 3y + 6 = 0.$

EXAMPLE 2. Find the equation of the straight line which passes through the points $(1, -5)$ and $(-4, 4)$.

Since the slope of this line is

$$m = \frac{4 + 5}{-4 - 1} = -\frac{9}{5},$$

then the equation is

$$y - (-5) = -\frac{9}{5}(x - 1),$$

$$5y + 25 = -9x + 9,$$

or $\qquad\qquad 9x + 5y + 16 = 0.$

E X E R C I S E S

Find the equations of the following lines:

1. Through $(2,5)$ with slope 2.

2. Through $(4, -1)$ with slope 5.

3. Through $(3,4)$ with slope -2.

4. Through $(1,5)$ with slope $-\frac{1}{4}$.

5. Through $(0, -3)$ with slope $-\frac{2}{3}$.

6. Through $(4,2)$ with slope $\frac{1}{3}$.

7. Through $(3, -2)$ with slope $-\frac{2}{5}$.

8. Through $(1,3)$ with slope $\frac{1}{4}$.

9. Through the origin with slope $-\frac{7}{9}$.

10. Through the origin with slope m.

11. Through $(\frac{3}{2}, -\frac{5}{3})$ with slope $\frac{4}{3}$.

12. Through $(0,b)$ with slope m.

13. Through $(1, -4)$ with inclination $\frac{\pi}{4}$.

14. Through $(-3, -5)$ with inclination $\frac{3\pi}{4}$.

15. Through $(5,7)$ and $(1,1)$.

16. Through $(-2,-4)$ and $(1,3)$.
17. Through $(-3,7)$ and $(5,-1)$.
18. Through $(5,0)$ and $(-2,3)$.
19. Through $(7,0)$ and $(0,-5)$.
20. Through $(a,0)$ and $(0,b)$.

3-5 Slope-Intercept Form

An important special case of the point-slope form of the equation of a straight line is obtained by selecting $(0,b)$ as the given point, where b is the y-intercept.

Then the equation of the line is,

$$y - b = m(x - 0),$$

or $$y = mx + b.$$

This is called the *slope-intercept* form of the equation of the straight line. In particular, this form of the equation is useful for sketching the line.

EXAMPLE 1. Find the equation of the line whose y-intercept is -7 and whose slope is $\frac{1}{2}$.

By substitution, $$y = \tfrac{1}{2}x - 7,$$

or $$x - 2y - 14 = 0.$$

EXAMPLE 2. Find the equation of the straight line, which is shown in Fig. 3-8.

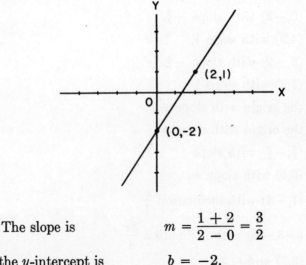

Fig. 3-8.

The slope is $$m = \frac{1+2}{2-0} = \frac{3}{2}$$

and the y-intercept is $$b = -2.$$

26 / The Straight Line

Therefore, the equation is

$$y = \frac{3}{2}x - 2$$

or $\qquad\qquad 3x - 2y - 4 = 0.$

EXAMPLE 3. Sketch the straight line whose equation is

$$3x + 4y + 4 = 0.$$

Write in slope-intercept form

$$y = -\tfrac{3}{4}x - 1$$

Hence, $\qquad\qquad m = -\tfrac{3}{4} \quad$ and $\quad b = -1.$

Start with the point $(0,-1)$ and lay off the slope $-\tfrac{3}{4}$, as in Fig. 3-9, by counting 4 units to the left and 3 units up to the point $(-4,2)$. The line joining these two points is the required line.

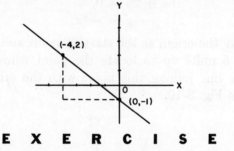

Fig. 3-9.

E X E R C I S E S

Find the equation of the straight line determined by each of the following sets of conditions.

1. y-intercept -5; slope 3.

2. y-intercept 4; slope -1.

3. y-intercept -2; slope $\tfrac{1}{3}$.

4. y-intercept 3; slope $-\tfrac{2}{3}$.

5. Crosses the y-axis at the point $(0,-7)$; angle of inclination $\dfrac{3\pi}{4}$.

Sketch the following lines, employing their slopes and y-intercepts:

6. $3x + y - 2 = 0.$

7. $2x - y - 5 = 0.$

8. $5x - y + 4 = 0.$

9. $3x + 4y + 8 = 0.$

10. $x - 4y + 12 = 0.$

11. $3x + y - 10 = 0.$

12. $4x - 3y + 14 = 0.$

13. $7x + 5y + 10 = 0.$

14. $3x + 3y - 8 = 0.$

15. $4x - 6y + 15 = 0.$

3-6 Lines Through the Origin

If a line passes through the origin, its equation is found by substituting the coordinates of the origin (0,0) in the point-slope form of the equation of a straight line.

Thus, $$y - 0 = m(x - 0),$$
or $$y = mx$$

EXAMPLE 1. Find the equation of the straight line through the origin with a slope equal to $-\frac{1}{3}$.

$$y = -\tfrac{1}{3}x,$$
$$3y = -x,$$
$$x + 3y = 0.$$

EXAMPLE 2. Sketch the line whose equation is $5x + 2y = 0$.

Since $$5x + 2y = 0,$$
$$y = -\tfrac{5}{2}x.$$

Accordingly, take the origin as the starting point and count 2 units to the left and 5 units up to locate the point whose coordinates are $(-2,5)$. The line joining this point with the origin is the required line, as in Fig. 3-10.

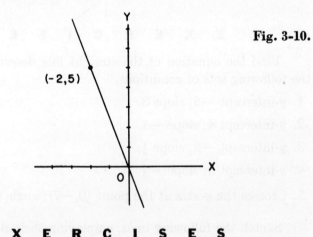

(-2,5)

Fig. 3-10.

E X E R C I S E S

Find the equations of the straight lines which pass through the origin and have the following slopes:

1. $\frac{1}{3}$.

2. $-\frac{2}{5}$.

3. -3.

4. $-\frac{3}{4}$.

5. $\frac{2}{7}$.

6. $-\frac{a}{b}$.

3-7 Lines Parallel to the Axes

(a) Parallel to the x-axis. If a line is parallel to the x-axis, its slope is zero and its equation becomes

$$y = 0 \cdot x + b$$

or $\qquad\qquad y = b,$

where b is the distance of the line from the x-axis.

(b) Parallel to the y-axis. If a line is parallel to the y-axis, its slope has no value and hence, the right member of the equation of the line has no meaning. However, since all points on this line are at the same distance a from the y-axis, its equation is $x = a$.

EXAMPLE. Find the equation of the straight line which passes through the point $(-5, -3)$ and is parallel to the x-axis.

Since the ordinate of the point $(-5, -3)$ is -3, then $b = -3$ and the equation of the line is $y = -3$, or $y + 3 = 0$.

E X E R C I S E S

Find the equation of the straight line which satisfies each of the following conditions:

1. Through $(7, -3)$; parallel to x-axis.

2. Through $(5, -2)$; parallel to x-axis.

3. Through $(-7, -5)$; parallel to y-axis.

4. Parallel to x-axis; 7 units below it.

5. Parallel to y-axis; 3 units to right of it.

3-8 General Equation of First Degree

The development in Sections 3-3 through 3-7 shows that every straight line can be represented by an algebraic equation of the first degree in x and y. Conversely, every algebraic equation of the first degree in x and y can be represented by a straight line.

To prove this, let $Ax + By + C = 0$, be an equation of the first degree in x and y, where A, B, and C are constants.

Solving for y, $\qquad\qquad y = -\dfrac{A}{B}x - \dfrac{C}{B}.$

A comparison of this equation with the slope-intercept form of the equation of the straight line, indicates the following facts:

(a) If $B \neq 0$, $Ax + By + C = 0$ is the equation of a straight line, whose slope is $- \dfrac{A}{B}$ and whose y-intercept is $- \dfrac{C}{B}$.

(b) If $B = 0$, the equation $Ax + By + C = 0$ reduces to $Ax + C = 0$, which is the equation of a straight line parallel to the y-axis and at a distance of $- \dfrac{C}{A}$ units from the axis.

In *either case*, the equation $Ax + By + C = 0$ is the equation of a *straight line*.

3-9 Parallel and Perpendicular Lines

(a) *Parallel.* If two lines are *parallel*, their slopes are equal and, conversely, if the slopes of two lines are equal, the lines are parallel.

The truth of these statements follows from an examination of Fig. 3-11, where l_1 and l_2 are two parallel lines.

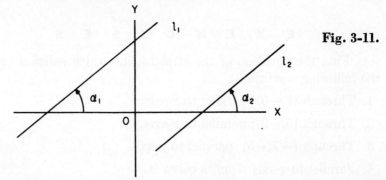

Fig. 3-11.

The angles of inclination α_1 and α_2 are equal, because they are corresponding angles of parallel lines cut by a transversal.

Since
$$m_1 = \tan \alpha_1 \quad \text{and} \quad m_2 = \tan \alpha_2,$$
then
$$m_1 = m_2.$$

If the steps of the above derivation are reversed, the converse of this theorem follows.

In the special case where the two lines are parallel to the y-axis, the slopes have no value, since the tangent of $\dfrac{\pi}{2}$ is not defined.

(b) *Perpendicular.* If the two lines are *perpendicular* to each other, the slope of either one is the negative reciprocal of the slope of the other, and conversely.

To prove these statements, let l_1 and l_2 be two perpendicular lines, as in Fig. 3-12.

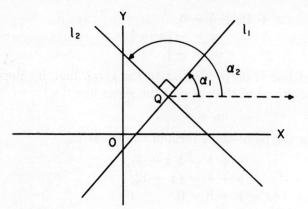

Fig. 3-12.

Since l_1 and l_2 are perpendicular to each other,

$$\alpha_2 = \frac{\pi}{2} + \alpha_1$$

and

$$\tan \alpha_2 = \tan \left(\frac{\pi}{2} + \alpha_1 \right).$$

Therefore,

$$\tan \alpha_2 = -\cot \alpha_1 = -\frac{1}{\tan \alpha_1}$$

But

$$m_1 = \tan \alpha_1 \quad \text{and} \quad m_2 = \tan \alpha_2.$$

Therefore,

$$m_2 = -\frac{1}{m_1} \quad \text{or} \quad m_1 m_2 = -1.$$

The proof of the converse of this theorem is left to the student.

Again, if the lines are parallel to the axes, one of the slopes has no value $\left(\text{tangent of } \frac{\pi}{2} \text{ is undefined} \right)$, however, in this special case, it is readily seen that the lines are perpendicular to each other.

EXAMPLE 1. Are the lines $2x - 3y - 2 = 0$ and $4x - 6y + 5 = 0$ parallel?

If

$$2x - 3y - 2 = 0,$$
$$y = \tfrac{2}{3}x - \tfrac{2}{3}.$$

Therefore its slope $m_1 = \tfrac{2}{3}$.

Also, if

$$4x - 6y + 5 = 0,$$
$$y = \tfrac{2}{3}x + \tfrac{5}{3}.$$

Therefore its slope $m_2 = \tfrac{2}{3}$.

Since the slopes are equal, the lines are parallel.

EXAMPLE 2. Find the equation of the line which passes through the point $(-3, -4)$ and is perpendicular to the line $x + 4y + 5 = 0$.

If
$$x + 4y + 5 = 0,$$
$$y = -\tfrac{1}{4}x - \tfrac{5}{4},$$
$$m_1 = -\tfrac{1}{4}.$$

Since the required line is perpendicular to the given line, its slope is the negative reciprocal of the slope of the given line, i.e.,

$$m_2 = 4.$$

By substitution in the point-slope form of the equation,

$$y + 4 = 4(x + 3),$$
$$y + 4 = 4x + 12,$$

and
$$4x - y + 8 = 0.$$

E X E R C I S E S

Determine which of the following pairs of lines are (a) parallel, (b) perpendicular, (c) neither:

1. $x - y + 3 = 0; x + y - 7 = 0.$

2. $4x - y + 5 = 0; 8x - 2y - 9 = 0.$

3. $5x + 3y - 8 = 0; 3x - 5y + 3 = 0.$

4. $x + 3y - 9 = 0; 2x - y + 4 = 0.$

5. $3x - 4y - 12 = 0; 8x + 6y - 1 = 0.$

6. $5x + 7y + 3 = 0; 6x - 3y + 2 = 0.$

7. $4x - 5y - 9 = 0; 8x - 10y + 7 = 0.$

Find the equations of each of the following straight lines:

8. Through $(3,1)$; parallel to $2x + 5y - 4 = 0.$

9. Through $(-1,-4)$; perpendicular to $2x - 3y - 4 = 0.$

10. Through $(7,1)$; perpendicular to $7x + 3y + 6 = 0.$

11. Through $(-1,3)$; parallel to $y = 5x.$

12. Through $(5,-2)$; parallel to the line through the points $(1,4)$ and $(-2,-7)$.

13. Through $(-1,7)$; perpendicular to the line through the points $(2,3)$ and $(0,-4)$.

14. Prove by the use of slopes that the points $(4,2)$, $(-3,7)$ and $(-1,-5)$ are the vertices of a right triangle.

15. Prove by the use of slopes that the points $(-4,3)$, $(-5,-3)$, $(2,-1)$, and $(3,5)$ are the vertices of a parallelogram.

16. Find the equation of the perpendicular bisector of the line segment joining the points (4,7) and (−2,1).

17. Prove by the use of slopes that the points (3,2), (4,4), and (−2,−8) lie on the same straight line.

18. Prove analytically that the altitudes of a triangle are concurrent (i.e., pass through the same point).

3-10 *Distance from a Point to a Line*

A method for finding the distance from a point to a line is illustrated by the following numerical example:

Let d be the perpendicular distance from the point $P(2,-3)$ to the line $l: 3x + 4y - 4 = 0$, as in Fig. 3-13.

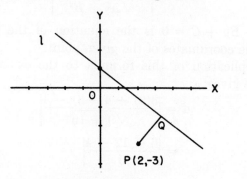

Fig. 3-13.

First, find the equation of the line PQ from $P(2,-3)$ and perpendicular to the given line $3x + 4y - 4 = 0$:

$$y = -\tfrac{3}{4}x + 1.$$

Therefore the slope of line l is

$$m_1 = -\tfrac{3}{4}$$

and the slope of PQ is

$$m_2 = \tfrac{4}{3}.$$

And the equation of PQ is

$$y + 3 = \tfrac{4}{3}(x - 2)$$

or

$$4x - 3y - 17 = 0.$$

To obtain the coordinates of the point of intersection of lines, l and PQ, it is necessary to solve their equations, simultaneously,

$$\begin{cases} 3x + 4y = 4, \\ 4x - 3y = 17. \end{cases}$$

From this solution,

$$x = \tfrac{16}{5} \quad \text{and} \quad y = -\tfrac{7}{5}.$$

Hence, the coordinates of the point of intersection are $(\tfrac{16}{5}, -\tfrac{7}{5})$.

Next use the "distance formula" to find the length of PQ,

$$d = \sqrt{(2 - \tfrac{16}{5})^2 + (-3 + \tfrac{7}{5})^2}$$
$$= \sqrt{(-\tfrac{6}{5})^2 + (-\tfrac{8}{5})^2}$$
$$= \sqrt{\frac{36 + 64}{25}} = \sqrt{\frac{100}{25}}$$

Therefore, $d = PQ = 2.$

However, a much simpler method for finding the distance from a point to a line is to use the formula, which is derived in Section 3-11:

$$d = \left| \frac{Ax_1 + By_1 + C}{\sqrt{A^2 + B^2}} \right|,$$

where $Ax + By + C = 0$ is the equation of the given line and (x_1, y_1) are the coordinates of the given point.

The application of this formula to the example which was solved above gives:

$$d = \left| \frac{3(2) + 4(-3) - 4}{\sqrt{9 + 16}} \right|$$

$$= \left| \frac{6 - 12 - 4}{5} \right|$$

$$= \left| \frac{-10}{5} \right| = \left| -2 \right| = 2.$$

E X E R C I S E S

Find the distance from the given point to the given line in each of the following:

1. $(3,2)$; $4x - 3y + 2 = 0$.

2. $(3,7)$; $3x + 4y - 2 = 0$.

3. $(-6,5)$; $5x - 12y + 12 = 0$.

4. $(3,-1)$; $5x + 12y - 16 = 0$.

5. $(-1,5)$; $4x + 3y = 0$.

6. $(0,0)$; $2x + 2y - 5 = 0$.

7. $(-7,3)$; $8x + 15y - 6 = 0$.

8. $(0, -3)$; $15x - 8y - 16 = 0$.

9. $(6, -2)$; $3x - 3y + 5 = 0$.

10. $(2, -7)$; $2x - 3y + 15 = 0$.

11. Find the length of the altitude from the vertex A to the side BC of the triangle whose vertices are $A(4,5)$, $B(-3,2)$, and $C(1,-4)$.

12. Find the area of triangle ABC which is given in Exercise 11.

13. Show that the line $3x - 4y - 8 = 0$ is tangent to the circle whose center is at the point $(7,-3)$ and whose radius is 5.

14. The distance from the point $(-2,3)$ to the line $4x + 3y + k = 0$, is 3. Find the value of k.

15. Find the distance between the two parallel lines

$$4x - 3y - 12 = 0 \quad \text{and} \quad 4x - 3y + 9 = 0$$

[*Hint:* Choose any point on one line and find its distance to the other line.]

3-11 *Proof of Formula for Distance from a Point to a Line (Optional)*

Let d be the distance from the point $P_1(x_1,y_1)$ to the line l: $Ax + By + C = 0$ (Fig. 3-14).

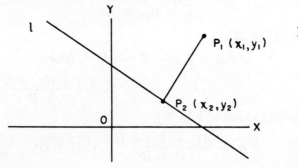

Fig. 3-14.

Let $P_2(x_2,y_2)$ be the foot of the perpendicular P_1P_2 from the given point P_1 to the line $Ax + By + C = 0$.

Since

$$y = -\frac{A}{B}x - \frac{C}{B},$$

the slope of l is

$$m_1 = -\frac{A}{B}.$$

Hence, the slope of P_1P_2 is

$$m_2 = \frac{B}{A}.$$

But the slope of P_1P_2 is
$$m_2 = \frac{y_2 - y_1}{x_2 - x_1}.$$

Therefore,
$$\frac{B}{A} = \frac{y_2 - y_1}{x_2 - x_1}$$

and
$$\frac{x_2 - x_1}{A} = \frac{y_2 - y_1}{B}.$$

Let each of the equal fractions be denoted by k.

Then
$$\frac{x_2 - x_1}{A} = k \quad \text{and} \quad \frac{y_2 - y_1}{B} = k,$$

and
$$x_2 - x_1 = Ak \quad \text{and} \quad y_2 - y_1 = Bk \qquad [1]$$

Now, find the length of P_1P_2 by the "distance formula,"
$$d^2 = (x_2 - x_1)^2 + (y_2 - y_1)^2.$$

By substitution, $\quad d^2 = A^2k^2 + B^2k^2,$

or
$$d = k\sqrt{A^2 + B^2} \qquad [2]$$

Now multiply the first equation of [1] by A and the second equation by B, and add.

Then
$$Ax_2 + By_2 - Ax_1 - By_1 = A^2k + B^2k \qquad [3]$$

Since $P_2(x_2, y_2)$ lies on the given line,
$$Ax_2 + By_2 + C = 0,$$

or,
$$Ax_2 + By_2 = -C. \qquad [4]$$

Substitute [4] in [3].

Then
$$-Ax_1 - By_1 - C = (A^2 + B^2)k$$

and
$$k = -\frac{Ax_1 + By_1 + C}{A^2 + B^2}.$$

Substitute this value of k in [2].

Then
$$d = -\frac{Ax_1 + By_1 + C}{A^2 + B^2} \cdot \sqrt{A^2 + B^2}.$$

Therefore,
$$d = \pm\frac{Ax_1 + By_1 + C}{\sqrt{A^2 + B^2}}.$$

Since, in general, P_1P_2 is parallel to neither axis, the distance d is considered essentially positive and the formula can be written
$$d = \left|\frac{Ax_1 + By_1 + C}{\sqrt{A^2 + B^2}}\right|.$$

4

CONIC SECTIONS

4-1 Introduction

The general equation of the second degree in x and y can be written in the form

$$Ax^2 + Bxy + Cy^2 + Dx + Ey + F = 0,$$

where A, B, and C are not all zero.

It is the purpose of this chapter to study the general equation of the second degree in x and y and to show that it always represents one of the following loci: circle, ellipse, parabola, hyperbola, or one of the limiting forms of these curves.

In this text, only those equations in which $B = 0$ are analyzed in detail. Hence, for this purpose, the general equation of the second degree in x and y is

$$Ax^2 + Cy^2 + Dx + Ey + F = 0. \qquad [1]$$

The curves which are represented by equation [1] are called *conic sections* because they can be obtained by cutting a right circular cone by a plane, a fact that was known to the ancient Greek mathematicians.

4-2 Equation of the Circle

A circle may be defined as the locus of a point which moves so that its distance from a fixed point is a constant. *Definition (KNOW)*

To find the equation of a circle, let $C(h,k)$ be the given point and r be the constant distance, as in Fig. 4-1.

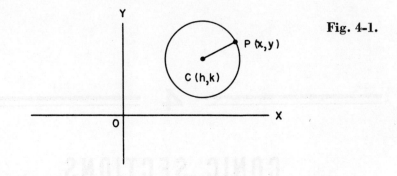

Fig. 4-1.

The point C is called the *center* and the distance CP is called the *radius*.

Further, let $P(x,y)$ be any point on the circle.

The "distance formula" shows that

$$\sqrt{(x-h)^2 + (y-k)^2} = r$$

and
$$(x-h)^2 + (y-k)^2 = r^2. \qquad [2]$$

If the center is at the origin, its coordinates are $(0,0)$ and then equation [2] becomes

$$x^2 + y^2 = r^2. \qquad [3]$$

EXAMPLE. Write the equation of the circle with its center at $(3,-1)$ and radius equal to 6.

Substitute in [2]:

$$(x-3)^2 + (y+1)^2 = 6^2,$$
$$x^2 - 6x + 9 + y^2 + 2y + 1 = 36,$$
and
$$x^2 + y^2 - 6x + 2y - 26 = 0.$$

E X E R C I S E S

Write the equations of the following circles:

1. Center at $(0,0)$; radius 5.

2. Center at $(0,0)$; radius 7.

3. Center at $(0,0)$; radius 4.

4. Center at $(0,0)$; radius 9.

5. Center at $(2,4)$; radius 5.

6. Center at $(-3,1)$; radius 4.

7. Center at $(9,-3)$; radius 3.

8. Center at $(-5,-3)$; radius 5.

9. Center at $(3,\frac{1}{2})$; radius 6.

10. Center at $(-\frac{3}{5},2)$; radius 5.

11. Center at $(\frac{7}{4},-\frac{9}{2})$; radius $\frac{1}{2}$.

12. Center at $(-\frac{3}{4},-3)$; radius 6.

13. Having $(-5,6)$ and $(1,-2)$ as the endpoints of a diameter. (midpoint)

14. Having the center at the origin and passing through the point $(4,-3)$.

15. Show that the equations $x = r \sin \theta$ and $y = r \cos \theta$ represent a circle with its center at the origin and its radius equal to r.

4-3 *Graph of the Circle*

By expansion and rearrangement, equation [2] becomes

$$x^2 + y^2 - 2hx - 2ky + h^2 + k^2 - r^2 = 0. \qquad [4]$$

This may be written

$$Ax^2 + Cy^2 + Dx + Ey + F = 0, \qquad [5]$$

where $A = C = 1; D = -2h; E = -2k;$ and

$$F = h^2 + k^2 - r^2.$$

When the equation of a circle is given in the form [5], it is possible to obtain its center and its radius by reducing the equation to form [2], as follows:

EXAMPLE 1. Find the center and the radius of the circle

$$x^2 + y^2 - 4x + 6y - 12 = 0$$

and sketch the figure.

Rewrite the given equation as

$$(x^2 - 4x \qquad) + (y^2 + 6y \qquad) = 12.$$

Complete the square in each parenthesis, and balance the equation:

$$(x^2 - 4x + 4) + (y^2 + 6y + 9) = 12 + 4 + 9$$

or
$$(x - 2)^2 + (y + 3)^2 = 25.$$

Since this equation is of form [2], the center of the circle is $C(2,-3)$ and the radius is 5. The graph of the circle is shown in Fig. 4-2.

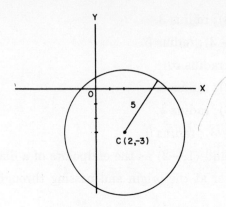

Fig. 4-2.

EXAMPLE 2. Find the center and the radius of the circle

$$4x^2 + 4y^2 + 24x - 8y + 15 = 0.$$

Divide by 4:

$$x^2 + y^2 + 6x - 2y + \tfrac{15}{4} = 0.$$

Rearrange:

$$(x^2 + 6x \qquad) + (y^2 - 2y \qquad) = -\tfrac{15}{4}$$

and

$$(x^2 + 6x + 9) + (y^2 - 2y + 1) = -\tfrac{15}{4} + 9 + 1,$$

or

$$(x + 3)^2 + (y - 1)^2 = \tfrac{25}{4}.$$

Therefore the center is at $C(-3,1)$ and the radius is $\tfrac{5}{2}$.

Note that if the right side of such an equation becomes 0, the circle reduces to a point and if the right side becomes negative, there is no circle.

E X E R C I S E S

Find the center and the radius of each of the following circles, and sketch the figure:

1. $x^2 + y^2 - 8x + 10y + 5 = 0.$

2. $x^2 + y^2 + 4x - 2y - 44 = 0.$

3. $x^2 + y^2 - 4x + 6y - 36 = 0.$

4. $x^2 + y^2 - 10x + 6y - 18 = 0.$

5. $x^2 + y^2 + 12x - 10y - 20 = 0.$

6. $x^2 + y^2 - 16x + 12y = 0.$

7. $x^2 + y^2 + 10x = 0.$

8. $x^2 + y^2 - 6x + 4y - 19 = 0.$

9. $x^2 + y^2 - 8y - 9 = 0.$

10. $4x^2 + 4y^2 - 12x + 4y - 15 = 0.$

11. $4x^2 + 4y^2 + 12x + 16y = 0.$

12. $5x^2 + 5y^2 - 2x - 3y = 0.$

13. $3x^2 + 3y^2 - 4x + 10y - 7 = 0.$

4-4 *Circles Determined by Given Conditions*

From the preceding discussion, it is seen that, for the equation [5] to be a circle, A must be equal to C. Then, by division, equation [5] becomes

$$x^2 + y^2 + \frac{D}{A}x + \frac{E}{A}y + \frac{F}{A} = 0. \qquad [6]$$

Since the quantities $\dfrac{D}{A}, \dfrac{E}{A},$ and $\dfrac{F}{A}$ are only different numbers,

the equation [6] is essentially of the form

$$x^2 + y^2 + Dx + Ey + F = 0. \qquad [7]$$

This equation may be called the *general form* of the equation of the circle.

Since there are three constants, D, E, and F in equation [7], any three geometric conditions which lead to three independent equations in D, E, and F will determine a circle. These three equations may be solved simultaneously, and the resulting values of D, E, and F give an equation of the form [7].

EXAMPLE.

Find the equation of the circle which passes through the points $(3, -3)$, $(0, -1)$, and $(3, -1)$.

The general form of the equation of the circle is

$$x^2 + y^2 + Dx + Ey + F = 0.$$

The coordinates of each of the points through which the circle passes must satisfy this equation.

Hence,
$$9 + 9 + 3D - 3E + F = 0,$$
$$0 + 1 \qquad\quad - E + F = 0,$$
$$9 + 1 + 3D - E + F = 0.$$

Solving these three equations simultaneously gives the values of

$$D = -3, \quad E = 4, \quad \text{and} \quad F = 3.$$

Then the equation is

$$x^2 + y^2 - 3x + 4y + 3 = 0.$$

E X E R C I S E S

Find the equation of the circle which passes through each of the following sets of three points:

1. $(0,0)$, $(4,4)$, and $(8,0)$.
2. $(1,0)$, $(-2,0)$, and $(0,4)$.
3. $(2,-4)$, $(4,0)$, and $(7,1)$.
4. $(1,0)$, $(5,0)$, and $(3,2)$.
5. $(-1,0)$, $(-1,-4)$, and $(3,-4)$.
6. $(3,6)$, $(-5,2)$, and $(4,-1)$.
7. $(1,4)$, $(2,-3)$, and $(3,0)$.
8. $(3,1)$, $(1,-3)$, and $(-6,-2)$.
9. $(4,1)$, $(-4,-3)$, and $(2,5)$.
10. Find the equation of a circle whose center is at $(-3,5)$ and is tangent to the line $4x - 3y - 18 = 0$.

4-5 *Equation of the Ellipse*

The *ellipse* may be defined as the locus of a point which moves so that the sum of its distances from two fixed points, called the *foci*, is a constant.

To derive the equation of the ellipse in its simplest form, let the line connecting the two foci, F_2 and F_1 (Fig. 4-3) be the x-axis and let the perpendicular bisector of the line segment, F_2F_1 be the y-axis. Also, let the distance between the foci be denoted by $2c$ and the constant distance by $2a$. Then, the coordinates of the foci are $(-c,0)$ and $(c,0)$.

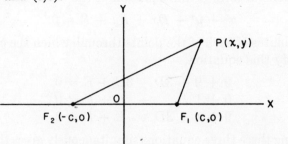

Fig. 4-3.

If $P(x,y)$ is any point of the ellipse, then the definition of the ellipse requires that

$$F_2P + F_1P = 2a.$$

Then $\qquad \sqrt{(x+c)^2 + y^2} + \sqrt{(x-c)^2 + y^2} = 2a.$

Transpose the second radical and square:

$$x^2 + 2cx + c^2 + y^2 = 4a^2 - 4a\sqrt{(x-c)^2 + y^2}$$
$$+ x^2 - 2cx + c^2 + y^2.$$

This simplifies to

$$4cx - 4a^2 = -4a\sqrt{(x-c)^2 + y^2}.$$

Division by 4 gives,

$$cx - a^2 = -a\sqrt{(x-c)^2 + y^2}.$$

Squaring again,

$$c^2x^2 - 2a^2cx + a^4 = a^2(x^2 - 2cx + c^2 + y^2).$$

This reduces to

$$(a^2 - c^2)x^2 + a^2y^2 = a^2(a^2 - c^2).$$

Division by $a^2(a^2 - c^2)$ gives

$$\frac{x^2}{a^2} + \frac{y^2}{a^2 - c^2} = 1. \qquad\qquad [1]$$

From the definition of the ellipse, $2a > 2c$. (The sum of two sides of a triangle is greater than the third side, as in Fig. 4-3.) Then $a > c$ and $a^2 > c^2$, and consequently $a^2 - c^2 > 0$. Now, let $b^2 = a^2 - c^2$, where b is a real number. Then equation [1] reduces to

$$\frac{x^2}{a^2} + \frac{y^2}{b^2} = 1. \qquad\qquad [2]$$

The line through the foci of the ellipse is called the *principal axis* of the ellipse and the points V_2 and V_1 where the principal axis intersects the ellipse are called the *vertices*. The segment, V_2V_1 of the principal axis is called the *major axis* of the ellipse. The midpoint of the major axis is called the *center* of the ellipse, which, in the case under consideration, is at the origin. The chord of the ellipse which passes through the center and is perpendicular to the major axis is called the *minor axis*. (See Fig. 4-4.)

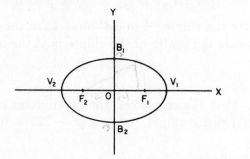

Fig. 4-4.

To find the coordinates of the vertices, set $y = 0$ in equation [2] and solve for x:

$$\frac{x^2}{a^2} + 0 = 1.$$

Therefore, $\qquad\qquad x^2 = a^2$

and $\qquad\qquad\qquad x = \pm a.$

Hence, the coordinates of V_2 and V_1 are $(-a,0)$ and $(a,0)$ and a is the length of the semi-major axis.

In a like manner, to find the coordinates of the endpoints of the minor axis, set $x = 0$ in equation [2] and solve for y:

$$0 + \frac{y^2}{b^2} = 1,$$

$$y^2 = b^2,$$
$$y = \pm b.$$

Hence, the coordinates of the endpoints of the minor axis (points B_2 and B_1, in Fig. 4-4) are $(0,-b)$ and $(0,b)$, and b is the length of the semi-minor axis.

From the relation $a^2 = b^2 + c^2$ it is possible to find any one of the quantities a, b, or c, when the other two are given.

The ratio $\frac{c}{a}$, which is the measure of the shape of the ellipse, is called the *eccentricity* and is denoted by e.

Thus, $\qquad\qquad\qquad e = \frac{c}{a}.$

Further, from the relation $c^2 = a^2 - b^2$, it is apparent that $c < a$. Hence, for the ellipse, e is always limited by the relation $0 < e < 1$.

Since equation [2] may be written in this form:

$$b^2x^2 + a^2y^2 - a^2b^2 = 0,$$

a comparison with the general equation of the second degree,

$$Ax^2 + Cy^2 + Dx + Ey + F = 0,$$

shows that, for the ellipse, A and C must have the same sign and, in the case where the center of the ellipse is at the origin,

$$D = E = 0.$$

EXAMPLE. Find the semi-axes, the coordinates of the foci, and the eccentricity of the ellipse, $9x^2 + 25y^2 - 225 = 0$, and sketch its curve.

Rearrange and divide by 225: $\dfrac{x^2}{25} + \dfrac{y^2}{9} = 1$.

Therefore, $a = 5$ and $b = 3$. Since $c^2 = a^2 - b^2$, $c^2 = 25 - 9 = 16$. Therefore, $c = 4$ and the coordinates of the foci are $(4,0)$ and $(-4,0)$. Also, the eccentricity is $e = \frac{4}{5}$, the vertices are at $(-5,0)$ and $(5,0)$, and the endpoints of the minor axis are at $(0,-3)$ and $(0,3)$. Thus, there are now four points for the sketching of the ellipse.

However, if additional points are desired for a more accurate sketching of the curve, the given equation may be solved for y,

$$25y^2 = 225 - 9x^2$$
$$= 9(25 - x^2).$$

Then
$$y^2 = \tfrac{9}{25}(25 - x^2)$$
and
$$y = \pm\tfrac{3}{5}\sqrt{25 - x^2}.$$
Hence,
$$\text{if } x = \quad 3,\ y = \pm\tfrac{12}{5};$$
$$x = -3,\ y = \pm\tfrac{12}{5};$$
$$x = \quad 4,\ y = \pm\tfrac{9}{5};$$
$$x = -4,\ y = \pm\tfrac{9}{5};\ \text{etc.}$$

Thus, additional points are available, if needed, although, in most cases, the two vertices and the two endpoints of the minor axis are sufficient to sketch the curve.

The curve may now be sketched, as in Fig. 4-5.

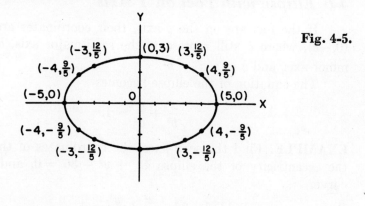

Fig. 4-5.

E X E R C I S E S

Find the semi-axes, the coordinates of the foci, and the eccentricity of the following ellipses, and sketch their curves:

1. $16x^2 + 25y^2 - 400 = 0$.

2. $25x^2 + 169y^2 - 4225 = 0$.

3. $4x^2 + 9y^2 - 36 = 0$.

4. $x^2 + 4y^2 - 16 = 0$.

5. $9x^2 + 25y^2 - 225 = 0$.

6. $x^2 + 9y^2 - 36 = 0$.

7. $2x^2 + 3y^2 - 12 = 0$.

8. $x^2 + 8y^2 - 32 = 0$.

9. $25x^2 + 64y^2 - 1600 = 0$.

10. $4x^2 + 25y^2 - 400 = 0$.

11. $3x^2 + 4y^2 - 9 = 0$.

12. $2x^2 + 3y^2 - 7 = 0$.

Find the equations of the following ellipses, whose centers are at the origin and which satisfy the given conditions:

13. Foci at $(\pm 4, 0)$; vertices at $(\pm 5, 0)$.

14. Foci at $(\pm 3, 0)$; length of minor axis = 6.

15. Endpoints of minor axis at $(0, \pm 3)$; distance between foci = 8.

16. Foci at $(\pm 5, 0)$; passes through point $(6, 0)$.

17. Foci at $(\pm 6, 0)$; eccentricity = $\frac{1}{2}$.

4-6 Ellipse with Foci on Y-Axis

If the foci are on the y-axis, their coordinates are $(0, c)$ and $(0, -c)$, where a still represents the semi-major axis, b the semi-minor axis, and $c = \sqrt{a^2 - b^2}$.

The equation of the ellipse becomes

$$\frac{x^2}{b^2} + \frac{y^2}{a^2} = 1.$$

EXAMPLE. Find the semi-axes, the coordinates of the foci, and the eccentricity of the ellipse $4x^2 + y^2 - 36 = 0$, and sketch its curve.

Rearrange and divide by 36: $\dfrac{x^2}{9} + \dfrac{y^2}{36} = 1$.

Here, $a = 6$ and $b = 3$, and the principal axis lies along the y-axis. Also, $c = \sqrt{36 - 9} = 3\sqrt{3}$, and the coordinates of the foci are $(0, 3\sqrt{3})$ and $(0, -3\sqrt{3})$. The eccentricity is $e = \dfrac{\sqrt{3}}{2}$.

From these facts, the ellipse may be sketched, as in Fig. 4-6.

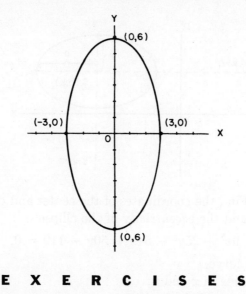

Fig. 4-6.

E X E R C I S E S

Find the semi-axes, the coordinates of the foci, and the eccentricity of the following ellipses, and sketch their curves:

1. $25x^2 + 9y^2 - 225 = 0$.

2. $9x^2 + 4y^2 - 36 = 0$.

3. $9x^2 + y^2 - 36 = 0$.

4. $4x^2 + y^2 - 80 = 0$.

5. $3x^2 + y^2 - 81 = 0$.

6. $4x^2 + y^2 - 9 = 0$.

7. $10x^2 + 2y^2 - 40 = 0$.

8. $12x^2 + 5y^2 - 45 = 0$.

4-7 Generalized Equation of the Ellipse

In the equation $\dfrac{x^2}{a^2} + \dfrac{y^2}{b^2} = 1$, a and b are the semi-major and the semi-minor axes of the ellipse and these are measured along the lines $x = 0$ and $y = 0$ (the coordinate axes) and from the point $(0,0)$ (the origin). Accordingly, the equation

$$\frac{(x - h)^2}{a^2} + \frac{(y - k)^2}{b^2} = 1$$

represents an ellipse whose axes are measured along the lines $y - k = 0$ and $x - h = 0$, from the point (h,k) as the center of the ellipse, as in Fig. 4-7.

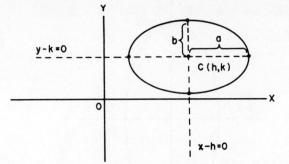

Fig. 4-7.

EXAMPLE. Find the coordinates of the center and of the foci and the semi-axes and the eccentricity of the ellipse

$$9x^2 + 25y^2 - 54x + 50y - 119 = 0,$$

and sketch its curve.

Collect terms in x and y:

$$9(x^2 - 6x \quad) + 25(y^2 + 2y \quad) = 119.$$

Complete the squares and balance the equation:

$$9(x^2 - 6x + 9) + 25(y^2 + 2y + 1) = 119 + 81 + 25$$

or, $$9(x - 3)^2 + 25(y + 1)^2 = 225.$$

Divide by 225: $$\frac{(x - 3)^2}{25} + \frac{(y + 1)^2}{9} = 1.$$

Therefore, the center of the ellipse is at the point $(3, -1)$ and the semi-axes are $a = 5$ and $b = 3$.

Therefore, the coordinates of the vertices are $V_1(8, -1)$ and $V_2(-2, -1)$, and those of the endpoints of the minor axis are $B_1(3,2)$ and $B_2(3, -4)$.

Since $c = 4$, the coordinates of the foci are $(-1, -1)$ and $(7, -1)$, and the eccentricity is $e = \frac{4}{5}$.

From these facts, the ellipse may be sketched as in Fig. 4-8.

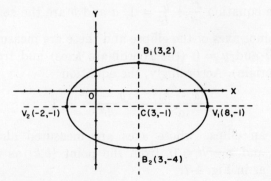

Fig. 4-8.

Find the coordinates of the center and of the foci, the semi-axes, and the eccentricity of the following ellipses, and sketch their curves:

1. $9x^2 + 25y^2 - 36x + 50y - 164 = 0.$

2. $4x^2 + 9y^2 - 32x + 36y + 64 = 0.$

3. $9x^2 + 16y^2 - 18x + 64y - 71 = 0.$

4. $x^2 + 4y^2 + 10x - 8y + 13 = 0.$

5. $9x^2 + 25y^2 - 100y - 125 = 0.$

6. $16x^2 + 9y^2 + 160x - 36y + 292 = 0.$

7. $4x^2 + y^2 + 16x - 6y - 39 = 0.$

8. $4x^2 + 25y^2 - 24x + 100y + 36 = 0.$

9. $x^2 + 9y^2 - 54y + 72 = 0.$

10. $4x^2 + y^2 + 24x + 2y + 1 = 0.$

11. $2x^2 + 18y^2 - 6x + 18y - 9 = 0.$

12. $16x^2 + 4y^2 + 12y - 7 = 0.$

4-8 *Equation of the Parabola*

A *parabola* may be defined as the locus of a point which moves so that its distance from a fixed point called the *focus* is always equal to its distance from a fixed line called the *directrix*.

To derive the equation of the parabola in its simplest form, let the line through the focus and perpendicular to the directrix be the x-axis and let the line which is perpendicular to the x-axis and midway between the focus and the directrix be the y-axis. Denote the distance from the directrix to the focus by $2p$.

Then, from Fig. 4-9, $QP = FP$.

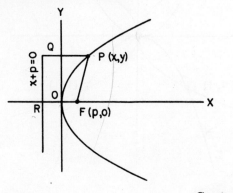

Fig. 4-9.

Let $P(x,y)$ be any point on the parabola. Then, since $QP = FP$, it follows that

$$x + p = \sqrt{(x - p)^2 + y^2}.$$

Squaring, $\quad x^2 + 2px + p^2 = x^2 - 2px + p^2 + y^2.$

Collecting terms, this equation reduces to

$$y^2 = 4px. \qquad [1]$$

The line through the focus and perpendicular to the directrix is called the *axis* of the parabola. The intersection of the axis with the parabola is called the *vertex* of the parabola.

In Fig. 4-9, the vertex is at the origin and the axis of the parabola lies along the x-axis. Also the line segment RF $(= 2p)$ is positive. However, if $2p$ is negative, the parabola opens to the left.

Further, if the vertex is at the origin and the axis of the parabola lies along the y-axis, the equation of the parabola becomes

$$x^2 = 4py. \qquad [2]$$

Here, the curve opens upward if $2p$ is positive and opens downward if $2p$ is negative.

Hence, when the vertex is at the origin, there are four positions that the parabola can assume. For example, the four related equations of a given parabola are

$$y^2 = x, \quad y^2 = -x, \quad x^2 = y, \quad \text{and} \quad x^2 = -y.$$

and the parabolas are illustrated in Fig. 4-10.

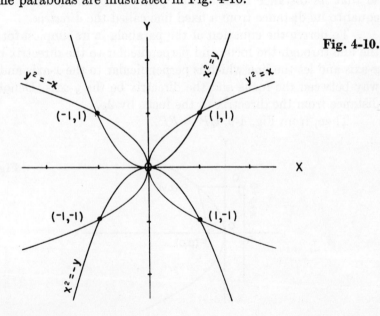

Fig. 4-10.

EXAMPLE 1. Sketch the parabola $x^2 = 4y$.

This is of the form of equation [2]. Hence the vertex of this parabola is at the origin, its axis lies on the y-axis and it opens upward. To obtain two additional points on the parabola, set $y = 1$ in the equation $x^2 = 4y$, obtaining $x = \pm 2$.

Accordingly, a sketch of the parabola is seen in Fig. 4-11.

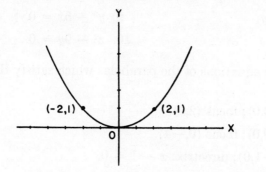

Fig. 4-11.

Further, since $4p = 4$, $p = 1$, the coordinates of the focus are $(0,1)$, and the equation of the directrix is $y + 1 = 0$.

EXAMPLE 2. Sketch the parabola $2y^2 = -x$.

Division by 2 gives $y^2 = -\frac{1}{2}x$, which is of the form of equation [1]. Therefore the vertex of this parabola is also at the origin, while its axis lies along the x-axis and it opens to the left. Further, if $x = -2$, $y = \pm 1$. From these data, the figure may be sketched as in Fig. 4-12.

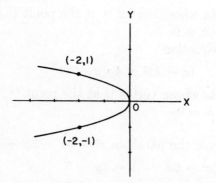

Fig. 4-12.

EXAMPLE 3. Find the equation of the parabola whose vertex is at the origin and whose focus is at the point $(0, -2)$.

Here $p = -2$ and $4p = -8$, and the equation is of the form $x^2 = 4py$. Therefore, its equation is $x^2 = -8y$.

Sketch the following parabolas:

1. $y^2 = 6x.$
2. $y^2 = -2x.$
3. $x^2 = 8y.$
4. $x^2 = -4y.$
5. $y^2 = 5x.$

6. $x^2 = -3y.$
7. $3x^2 = y.$
8. $3y^2 = -x.$
9. $y^2 + 5x = 0.$
10. $x^2 - 9y = 0.$

Find the equations of the parabolas which satisfy the following conditions:

11. Vertex $(0,0)$; focus $(2,0)$.
12. Vertex $(0,0)$; focus $(0,-4)$.
13. Focus $(-1,0)$; directrix: $x - 1 = 0$.
14. Vertex at origin; focus $(\frac{1}{2},0)$.
15. Vertex $(0,0)$; passes through point $(8,1)$.

4-9 *Generalized Equation of the Parabola*

In the equation $y^2 = 4px$ the line $y = 0$ (the x-axis) is the axis of the parabola and the point $(0,0)$ (the origin) is the vertex of the parabola. Accordingly, the equation

$$(y - k)^2 = 4p(x - h)$$

represents a parabola whose vertex is at the point (h,k) and whose axis is the line: $y - k = 0$.

Similarly, the equation

$$(x - h)^2 = 4p(y - k)$$

represents a parabola whose vertex is at the point (h, k) and whose axis is the line $x - h = 0$.

EXAMPLE 1. Sketch the parabola $x^2 - 6x - 2y + 5 = 0.$

Rearrange: $(x^2 - 6x\quad) = 2y - 5.$

Complete the square:

$$(x^2 - 6x + 9) = 2y - 5 + 9$$

or $\qquad (x - 3)^2 = 2(y + 2).$

This represents a parabola whose vertex is at the point $(3,-2)$ and whose axis is the line $x - 3 = 0$. Further, this parabola has exactly the same shape as the parabola $x^2 = 2y$, where, if $y = 2$, then $x = \pm 2$. Hence, to find two points, other than the vertex, through which the parabola passes, it is only necessary to count 2 units up from the vertex $(3, -2)$ and 2 units to both the right and left of the vertex to obtain the points $(1,0)$ and $(5,0)$. With these data the parabola may be sketched, as in Fig. 4-13.

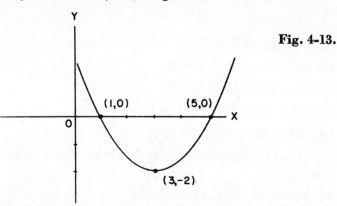

Fig. 4-13.

EXAMPLE 2. Find the equation of the parabola whose vertex is at the point $(-4,3)$ and whose focus is at the point $(-3,3)$.

Since the distance from the vertex to the focus is equal to p, then $p = 1$ and $4p = 4$. The axis of the parabola is the line: $y - 3 = 0$. Hence the equation of the parabola is

$$(y - 3)^2 = 4(x + 4),$$

or
$$y^2 - 6y + 9 = 4x + 16$$

and
$$y^2 - 4x - 6y - 7 = 0.$$

A comparison of the equations in Examples 1 and 2, namely,

$$x^2 - 6x - 2y + 5 = 0$$

and
$$y^2 - 4x - 6y - 7 = 0$$

with the general equation of the conic,

$$Ax^2 + Cy^2 + Dx + Ey + F = 0,$$

shows that, in the case of the parabola, either A or C must be equal to 0. Also, if $A = 0$, then $D \neq 0$, or if $C = 0$, then $E \neq 0$

E X E R C I S E S

Sketch the following parabolas:

1. $x^2 + 4x - y + 5 = 0.$

2. $y^2 - x - 2y - 1 = 0.$

3. $y^2 - 4x + 2y + 9 = 0.$

4. $y^2 - 8x - 6y + 17 = 0.$

5. $x^2 - 2x + y - 5 = 0.$

6. $2x^2 - 4x - y + 3 = 0.$

7. $x^2 + 4y - 8 = 0.$

8. $y^2 + 2x + 15 = 0.$

9. $x^2 - 4y + 4 = 0.$

10. $x^2 - 6x - 8y + 9 = 0.$

11. $x^2 - 6x - 4y + 5 = 0.$

12. $2x^2 - 10x - 2y + 11 = 0.$

13. $2x^2 - 12x + y + 21 = 0.$

Find the equations of the parabolas which satisfy the following conditions:

14. Vertex at $(0,1)$; focus at $(0,2)$.

15. Focus at $(3,2)$; directrix: $y + 2 = 0.$

16. Vertex at $(3,-1)$; focus at $(3,0)$.

17. Vertex at $(-1,-1)$; directrix: $x + 2 = 0.$

18. Axis parallel to the y-axis and vertex at $(-2,1)$ and passing through the point $(2,-1)$.

4-10 Equation of the Hyperbola

The *hyperbola* may be defined as the locus of a point which moves so that the difference of its distances from two fixed points, called the *foci*, is always a constant.

To derive the equation of the hyperbola, let the line which connects the two foci F_2 and F_1 (Fig. 4-14) be the x-axis and the point midway between the foci be the origin. Also, let the distance between the foci be denoted by $2c$ and the constant difference by

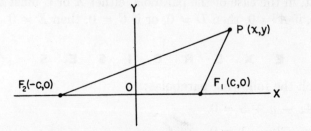

Fig. 4-14.

2a. Then the coordinates of the foci are $(-c,0)$ and $(c,0)$.

If $P(x, y)$ is any point on the hyperbola, the definition of the hyperbola requires that

$$F_2P - F_1P = 2a.$$

Then, by the "distance formula,"

$$\sqrt{(x + c)^2 + y^2} - \sqrt{(x - c)^2 + y^2} = 2a.$$

This equation is similar in form to the equation of the ellipse (see Section 4-5). Hence, a similar reduction gives the result

$$\frac{x^2}{a^2} - \frac{y^2}{c^2 - a^2} = 1 \qquad\qquad [1]$$

In the triangle F_2PF_1 (Fig. 4-14),

$$F_2P - F_1P < F_2F_1$$

since the difference between any two sides of a triangle is less than the third side.

But $\qquad\qquad F_2P - F_1P = 2a$

and $\qquad\qquad\qquad F_2F_1 = 2c.$

Therefore, $\qquad\quad 2a < 2c \quad$ and $\quad a < c,$

and $\qquad\qquad\qquad c^2 - a^2 > 0.$

Since $c^2 - a^2$ is a positive quantity, let $b^2 = c^2 - a^2$, where b is a real number.

Then equation [1] reduces to

$$\frac{x^2}{a^2} - \frac{y^2}{b^2} = 1 \qquad\qquad [2]$$

The line joining the foci of the hyperbola is called the *principal axis* of the hyperbola and the points V_2 and V_1, where the principal axis intersects the hyperbola, are called the *vertices*.

The segment V_2V_1 of the principal axis is called the *transverse axis* of the hyperbola. The midpoint of the transverse axis is called the *center* of the hyperbola which, in the case under consideration, is the origin.

To find the coordinates of the vertices, set $y = 0$ in equation [2] and solve for x:

$$\frac{x^2}{a^2} - 0 = 1,$$

$$x^2 = a^2,$$

$$x = \pm a.$$

Therefore, the coordinates of V_2 and V_1 are $(-a,0)$ and $(a,0)$, and a is the length of the semi-transverse axis.

To find the y-intercepts (if any), set $x = 0$ in equation [2] and solve for y:

$$0 - \frac{y^2}{b^2} = 1,$$

$$y^2 = -b^2.$$

Therefore, there are *no* real values for y and the curve has *no* y-intercepts.

From the relation $b^2 = c^2 - a^2$ it is possible to find any one of the quantities a, b, or c when the other two are given.

As in the case of the ellipse, the ratio $\frac{c}{a}$, which is called the *eccentricity* (e), is a measure of the shape of the hyperbola. Since, for the hyperbola, $c > a$, then $e = \frac{c}{a} > 1$.

4-11 *Asymptotes of the Hyperbola*

An *asymptote* to a curve is a straight line to which the curve gets closer and closer but never reaches or crosses.

From $$\frac{x^2}{a^2} - \frac{y^2}{b^2} = 1,$$

$$y^2 = \frac{b^2}{a^2}(x^2 - a^2),$$

$$y = \pm \frac{b}{a}\sqrt{x^2 - a^2}. \qquad [3]$$

Since a is a real number,

$$\sqrt{x^2 - a^2} < |\sqrt{x^2}|,$$

and $$\sqrt{x^2 - a^2} < |x|.$$

Therefore, from [3], $$|y| < \frac{b}{a}x.$$

As x increases without limit, the difference between $\sqrt{x^2 - a^2}$ and $|x|$ diminishes toward zero and so y approaches $\frac{b}{a}x$, both positively and negatively.

Therefore, the lines

$$y = \frac{b}{a}x \quad \text{and} \quad y = -\frac{b}{a}x$$

are the asymptotes of the hyperbola.

The asymptotes are a convenient guide for a sketching of the hyperbola.

Further, since equation [2] may be written in the form

$$b^2x^2 - a^2y^2 - a^2b^2 = 0,$$

a comparison with the general equation

$$Ax^2 + Cy^2 + Dx + Ey + F = 0$$

shows that, for the hyperbola, A and C must have opposite signs. Also $D = E = 0$, when the center of the hyperbola is at the origin.

EXAMPLE 1. Find the semi-axes, the coordinates of the foci, the eccentricity, and the equations of the asymptotes of the hyperbola $4x^2 - 9y^2 - 36 = 0$, and sketch its curve.
Rearrange and divide by 36:

$$\frac{x^2}{9} - \frac{y^2}{4} = 1.$$

Then, $a = 3, \quad b = 2, \quad c = \sqrt{13}, \quad e = \dfrac{\sqrt{13}}{3},$

and the asymptotes are the lines $y = \pm\frac{2}{3}x$.

From these data, the hyperbola may be sketched, as in Fig. 4-15.

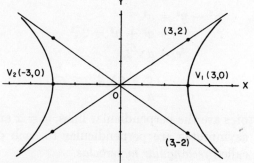

Fig. 4-15.

If the transverse axis of the hyperbola lies along the y-axis, then a still represents the semi-transverse axis, the coordinates of the vertices are $(0,-a)$ and $(0,a)$, and the coordinates of the foci are $(0,-c)$ and $(0,c)$.

In this case, the equation of the hyperbola becomes

$$\frac{y^2}{a^2} - \frac{x^2}{b^2} = 1$$

and the equations of the asymptotes are $y = \pm\dfrac{a}{b}x$.

EXAMPLE 2. Find the semi-transverse axis, the coordinates of the foci, the eccentricity, and the equations of the asymptotes of the hyperbola $x^2 - 4y^2 + 4 = 0$, and sketch its curve.

Rearrange and divide by 4: $\dfrac{y^2}{1} - \dfrac{x^2}{4} = 1$.

Here, the principal axis lies along the y-axis and $a = 1$, $b = 2$, $c = \sqrt{5}$, $e = \sqrt{5}$ and the equations of the asymptotes are $y = \pm\frac{1}{2}x$.

From these data, the hyperbola may be sketched, as in Fig. 4-16.

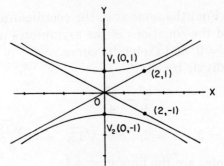

Fig. 4-16.

When $a = b$, the equation of the hyperbola reduces to the form

$$x^2 - y^2 = a^2. \qquad [4]$$

Here, $\qquad c^2 = a^2 + a^2 = 2a^2$

and $\qquad c = a\sqrt{2}.$

Also $\qquad e = \dfrac{c}{a} = \dfrac{a\sqrt{2}}{a} = \sqrt{2}$

and the asymptotes are the perpendicular lines, $y = x$ and $y = -x$.

Since the asymptotes are perpendicular to each other, these hyperbolas are called *rectangular hyperbolas*.

E X E R C I S E S

Find the semi-transverse axis, the coordinates of the foci, the eccentricity, and the equations of the asymptotes of the following hyperbolas, and sketch their curves:

1. $x^2 - 9y^2 - 9 = 0$.

2. $x^2 - 9y^2 - 36 = 0$.

3. $4x^2 - 9y^2 - 36 = 0$.

4. $9x^2 - 16y^2 - 144 = 0$.

5. $4x^2 - 9y^2 + 144 = 0.$

6. $x^2 - 2y^2 - 18 = 0.$

7. $25x^2 - 9y^2 - 225 = 0.$

8. $9y^2 - x^2 - 36 = 0.$

9. $y^2 - 4x^2 - 100 = 0.$

10. $x^2 - y^2 - 9 = 0.$

11. $x^2 - y^2 + 16 = 0.$

12. $3x^2 - 3y^2 + 4 = 0.$

13. $2x^2 - 3y^2 - 5 = 0.$

Find the equations of the hyperbolas which are determined by the following conditions:

14. Vertices $(\pm 4,0)$; foci $(\pm 6,0)$.

15. Foci $(\pm 4,0)$; eccentricity $= 2$.

16. Vertices $(0,\pm 4)$; eccentricity $= \frac{3}{2}$.

17. Foci $(0,\pm 5)$; semi-transverse axis $= 4$.

18. Foci $(\pm 4,0)$; distance between vertices $= 4$.

19. Rectangular hyperbola; foci $(\pm \sqrt{2},0)$.

20. Rectangular hyperbola; foci $(0,\pm 5)$.

4-12 *Hyperbola of the Form xy = k*

Since the asymptotes of a rectangular hyperbola are perpendicular to each other, it is often desirable to refer such hyperbolas to their asymptotes as coordinate axes.

By a derivation which is beyond the scope of this text, such hyperbolas have the form $xy = k$.

When k is positive, i.e. $k > 0$, the principal axis of the hyperbola makes an angle of $\frac{\pi}{4}$ with the coordinate axes and has the equation $y = x$, as in Fig. 4-17a. Since the vertices of an hyperbola are the points of intersection of the curve with its principal axis, the coordinates of these vertices are found by solving simultaneously the equations $xy = k$ and $x - y = 0$.

By substitution,
$$x \cdot x = k,$$
$$x^2 = k,$$
$$x = \pm \sqrt{k},$$
And, since $y = x$,
$$y = \pm \sqrt{k}.$$

Therefore, the coordinates of the vertices, V_1 and V_3 are $V_1(\sqrt{k},\sqrt{k})$ and $V_3(-\sqrt{k},-\sqrt{k})$.

Fig. 4-17a.

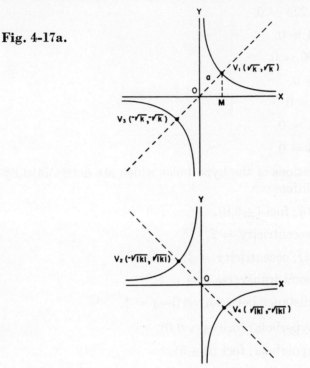

Fig. 4-17b.

If k is negative, i.e., $k < 0$, then the hyperbola exists in the second and the fourth quadrants, as shown in Fig. 4-17b. Here, the coordinates of the vertices V_2 and V_4 are $V_2(-\sqrt{|k|},\sqrt{|k|})$ and $V_4(\sqrt{|k|},-\sqrt{|k|})$. In either case, for $k > 0$ or $k < 0$, the distance OV, which is the semi-transverse axis, a, of the hyperbola, equals $\sqrt{|2k|}$, as is seen from an examination of triangle OV_1M in Fig. 4-17a.

The above statements are clarified by a "point-by-point" plotting of equations of the form, $xy = k$ for the two cases, where (a) $k > 0$ (Fig. 4-18) and (b) $k < 0$ (Fig. 4-19).

(a) Consider the equation $xy = 9$.

Since $y = \dfrac{9}{x}$, the following table of related values of x and y may be constructed:

x	1	2	3	$4\frac{1}{2}$	9	-1	-2	-3	$-4\frac{1}{2}$	-9
y	9	$4\frac{1}{2}$	3	2	1	-9	$-4\frac{1}{2}$	-3	-2	-1

Note that when $x = 0$, y is nonexistent.

Figure 4-18 is the graph of these values of x and y.

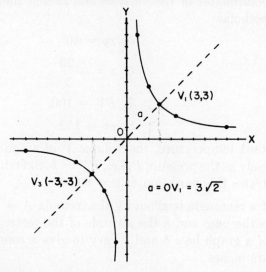

Fig. 4-18.

$V_1 (3,3)$

a

$V_3 (-3,-3)$

$a = OV_1 = 3\sqrt{2}$

(b) Consider the equation $xy = -4$.

Since $y = -\dfrac{4}{x}$, the following table may be constructed:

x	$\frac{1}{2}$	1	2	4	8	$-\frac{1}{2}$	-1	-2	-4	-8
y	-8	-4	-2	-1	$-\frac{1}{2}$	8	4	2	1	$\frac{1}{2}$

Figure 4-19 is the graph of these values of x and y.

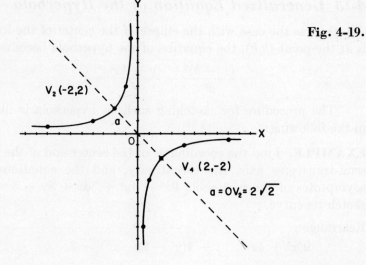

Fig. 4-19.

$V_2 (-2,2)$

a

$V_4 (2,-2)$

$a = OV_2 = 2\sqrt{2}$

Find the coordinates of the vertices and sketch the following rectangular hyperbolas:

1. $xy = 4$.

2. $xy = -9$.

3. $xy = 16$.

4. $xy = -8$.

5. $xy = 10$.

6. $x = -\dfrac{25}{y}$.

7. $PV = 100$.

8. $pr = 150$.

9. For a constant temperature, the volume V of an enclosed gas varies inversely as the pressure P, i.e., $PV = k$. Sketch the curve which illustrates this variation, if $k = 800$.

10. The area of a rectangle is given by the formula $A = bh$, where b represents the base and h the altitude of the rectangle. Show by means of a graph how b and h vary to give a constant area of 100 square inches.

Find the coordinates of the center and vertices of the following rectangular hyperbolas. [*Hint:* Rewrite the equations in form of $(x - h)(y - k) = $ a constant.]

11. $xy + 2x - 3y - 10 = 0$.

12. $xy + 3x - 4y - 3 = 0$.

13. $xy - 3x + 2y - 11 = 0$.

14. $xy - 2x - 5y + 1 = 0$.

4-13 Generalized Equation of the Hyperbola

As was the case with the ellipse, if the center of the hyperbola is at the point (h, k), the equation of the hyperbola becomes

$$\frac{(x - h)^2}{a^2} - \frac{(y - k)^2}{b^2} = 1. \tag{5}$$

The procedure for sketching such an hyperbola is illustrated in the following:

EXAMPLE. Find the coordinates of the center and of the foci, the semi-transverse axis, the eccentricity, and the equations of the asymptotes of the hyperbola $9x^2 - 4y^2 + 36x + 8y - 4 = 0$, and sketch its curve.

Rearrange:

$$9(x^2 + 4x \quad) - 4(y^2 - 2y \quad) = 4.$$

Complete squares and balance the equation:

$$9(x^2 + 4x + 4) - 4(y^2 - 2y + 1) = 4 + 36 - 4$$

and

$$9(x + 2)^2 - 4(y - 1)^2 = 36.$$

Divide by 36:

$$\frac{(x + 2)^2}{4} - \frac{(y - 1)^2}{9} = 1.$$

By comparison with equation [5], it is seen that $a = 2$, $b = 3$, $c = \sqrt{13}$, $e = \dfrac{\sqrt{13}}{2}$, and the slopes of the asymptotes are $\pm\frac{3}{2}$.

Consequently, the equations of the asymptotes are

$$(y - 1) = \pm\tfrac{3}{2}(x + 2),$$

or $3x - 2y + 8 = 0$ and $3x + 2y + 4 = 0$.

The coordinates of the center are $(-2,1)$, and the coordinates of the vertices are $(-4,1)$ and $(0,1)$.

From these data the curve is sketched as in Fig. 4-20.

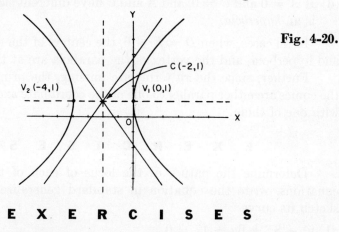

Fig. 4-20.

E X E R C I S E S

Find the coordinates of the center and the foci, the semi-transverse axis, the eccentricity, and the equations of the asymptotes of the following hyperbolas, and sketch their curves:

1. $4x^2 - 9y^2 - 32x + 36y - 8 = 0$.

2. $x^2 - 4y^2 + 10x - 16y + 25 = 0$.

3. $9x^2 - 16y^2 + 18x - 64y - 199 = 0$.

4. $4x^2 - 9y^2 - 24x - 54y - 81 = 0$.

5. $4x^2 - y^2 + 24x + 8y + 16 = 0$.

6. $x^2 - y^2 + 4x + 8y - 11 = 0$.

7. $16x^2 - 25y^2 - 64x - 336 = 0$.

8. $16x^2 - 9y^2 - 160x - 18y + 247 = 0$.

9. $16x^2 - 36y^2 + 48x + 180y - 225 = 0$.

10. $36x^2 - 100y^2 + 216x + 99 = 0$.

4-14 Summary

In the preceding discussion it was seen that the general equation of the second degree in x and y, with the xy term missing,

$$Ax^2 + Cy^2 + Dx + Ey + F = 0,$$

always represents one of the following loci: circle, ellipse, parabola, hyperbola or one of the limiting forms of these curves, as follows:

(a) If $A = C$, the locus is a *circle*.

(b) If $A \neq 0$ and $C \neq 0$, and A and C have the same signs, the locus is an *ellipse*. $a > b$

(c) If $A = 0$ and $C \neq 0$, or $A \neq 0$ and $C = 0$, the locus is a *parabola*.

(d) If $A \neq 0$ and $C \neq 0$, and A and C have different signs, the locus is an *hyperbola*. whatever letter over a then that is major axis,

In all cases, when $D = E = 0$, the centers of the circle, ellipse, and hyperbola, and the vertex of the parabola are at the origin.

Further, since the xy terms are missing, the principal axes of the conics are either parallel to one of the coordinate axes or coincide with one of them.

E X E R C I S E S

Determine the nature of the locus of each of the following equations, write the equation in standard generalized form, and sketch its curve:

1. $y^2 - 8x + 6y + 17 = 0$.

2. $4x^2 + 4y^2 - 12x + 16y - 11 = 0$.

3. $4x^2 + y^2 + 24x - 4y + 24 = 0$.

4. $4x^2 - y^2 - 40x - 4y + 80 = 0$.

5. $x^2 + y^2 - 10x = 0$.

6. $x^2 - y^2 + 6x + 4y - 4 = 0$.

7. $2x^2 + y^2 - 4x + 4y - 12 = 0$.

8. $25x^2 - 16y^2 + 200x + 96y + 656 = 0$.

9. $x^2 - 10x + 8y + 1 = 0$.

10. $5x^2 + 3y^2 + 20x - 12y + 2 = 0$.

5

CURVE TRACING

5-1 Introduction

As previously stated, the locus of an equation is the curve which contains all the points whose coordinates satisfy the equation.

One way to find the locus of an equation is to plot a sufficient number of points whose coordinates satisfy the given equation.

In this chapter, consideration is given to the graphs of some important equations which are neither straight lines nor conics.

5-2 Equations Involving Absolute Values

(a) $y = |x|$.

This is the equation $y = x$ when $x \geq 0$ and the equation $y = -x$ when $x < 0$.

A brief table of corresponding values of x and y may be constructed, as follows:

x	-5	-2	0	2	5
y	5	2	0	2	5

From these values of x and y, the graph in Fig. 5-1 may be constructed.

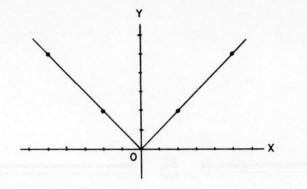

Fig. 5-1.

(b) $y = |x| + 1$.

This is the equation $y = x + 1$ when $x \geq 0$ and the equation $y = -x + 1$ when $x < 0$.

Hence:

x	-4	-2	0	2	4
y	5	3	1	3	5

And the graph is as in Fig. 5-2.

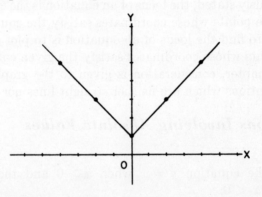

Fig. 5-2.

(c) $y = |x + 1|$.

Here the equation is $y = x + 1$ when $x \geq -1$ and the equation is $y = -(x + 1)$ when $x < -1$. A table of values of x and y is:

x	-4	-2	-1	0	2	4
y	3	1	0	1	3	5

and the graph is shown in Fig. 5-3.

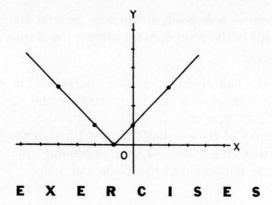

Fig. 5-3.

E X E R C I S E S

Sketch the graphs of the following equations:

1. $y = |x|$.

2. $y = |x - 1|$.

3. $y = |x| - 1$.

4. $y = |2x|$.

5. $y = |2x| + 1$.

6. $y = |2x + 1|$.

7. $y = |2x| - 1$.

8. $y = |2x - 1|$.

9. $y = |3x| - 2$.

10. $|x| + |y| = 1$.

5-3 *Equations of the Form* $y = x^n$

Two cases of equations of the form $y = x^n$ are to be considered:

(a) Where n is a positive integer, not zero, such as $y = x$, $y = x^2$, $y = x^3$, $y = x^4$, etc. The graphs of all of these equations pass through the points $(0,0)$, $(1,1)$, and either $(-1,1)$ or $(-1,-1)$, depending upon whether n is even or odd, as illustrated in Figs. 5-4a and 5-4b.

Fig. 5-4a.

Fig. 5-4b.

(b) Where n is a positive fraction. Several simple cases are given to illustrate the procedure for finding the graphs of equations of this form.

EXAMPLE 1. The equation $y^2 = x$ (parabola), $y^3 = x$ (cubical parabola), $y^4 = x$, $y^5 = x$ can be written in the form $y = \pm x^{\frac{1}{2}}$, $y = x^{\frac{1}{3}}$, $y = \pm x^{\frac{1}{4}}$, $y = x^{\frac{1}{5}}$.

The graphs of these equations pass through the points $(0,0)$, $(1,1)$, and either $(1,-1)$ or $(-1,-1)$, depending upon whether n is even or odd, as illustrated in Figs. 5-5a and 5-5b.

Fig. 5-5a.　　　　　　　　　　　　　　　　　　**Fig. 5-5b.**

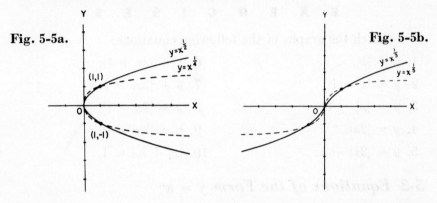

EXAMPLE 2. $y^2 = x^3$ (the semi-cubical parabola) may be written $y = \pm x^{\frac{3}{2}}$.

A short table of comparative values of x and y may be constructed, as follows:

x	0	1	4	9
y	0	± 1	± 8	± 27

The resulting graph is seen in Fig. 5-6.

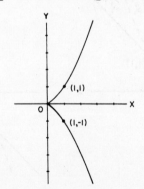

Fig. 5-6.

EXAMPLE 3. $y^3 = x^2$ is another form of the semi-cubical parabola and can be written in the form $y = x^{\frac{2}{3}}$.

A table of comparative values of x and y may be constructed:

x	0	±1	±8	±27
y	0	1	4	9

The resulting graph is seen in Fig. 5-7.

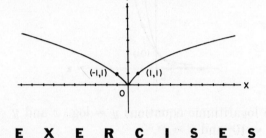

Fig. 5-7.

E X E R C I S E S

Sketch the graphs of the following equations:

1. $y = x^2$.
2. $y^2 = x^3$.
3. $y^3 = x^2$.
4. $y = x^6$.
5. $y^5 = x^2$.

6. $y = x^5$.
7. $y = 2x^3$.
8. $y = -x^3$.
9. $y^2 = 2x^3$.
10. $y^3 = -2x^2$.

5-4 *Exponential and Logarithmic Functions*

(a) The two most important examples of the exponential equation $y = a^x$ are $y = 10^x$ and $y = e^x$, where 10 is the base of the common system of logarithms and e (2.71828 . . . . .) is the base of the natural system of logarithms.

A short table of corresponding values of x and y from the equations $y = 10^x$ and $y = e^x$ may be constructed, as follows:

x	$y = 10^x$	$y = e^x$
0	1	1
1	10	2.72
2	100	7.39
−1	0.1	0.37
−2	0.01	0.14

In both these equations, as x decreases indefinitely, y approaches 0 as a limit. Hence, the x-axis is an asymptote of both of the curves. The resulting graphs of both of these equations are seen in Fig. 5-8.

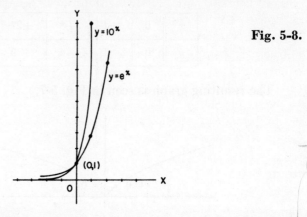

Fig. 5-8.

(b) The logarithmic equations $y = \log_{10} x$ and $y = \log_e x$ can be written $x = 10^y$ and $x = e^y$.

These are the exponential equations which were considered in the preceding paragraph, with the variables x and y interchanged. Accordingly, the graphs of the logarithmic equations are obtained from the graphs of the inverse exponential equations by interchanging the x- and the y-axes, as in Fig. 5-9.

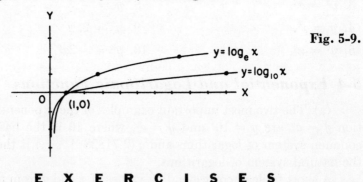

Fig. 5-9.

E X E R C I S E S

Sketch the graphs of the following equations:

1. $y = e^x$.

2. $y = 10^x$.

3. $y = 2^x$.

4. $y = \log_e x$.

5. $y = \log_{10} x$.

6. $y = \log_e \sqrt{x}$.

7. $y = \log_{10} \sqrt{x}$.

8. $y = \log_e x^2$.

9. $y = \log_{10} x^2$.

10. $y = (\tfrac{1}{2})^x$.

5-5 Sketching Algebraic Equations of Degree Greater than Second

In general, equations which do not fit in any of the preceding categories, can be plotted point by point, as indicated in Chapter 2. However, the work of sketching the graph may be simplified by noting certain properties of the graph from an examination of the equation. These properties are: (a) Symmetry, (b) Intercepts, (c) Domain and Range, and (d) Asymptotes.

(a) *Symmetry*. Two points are said to be symmetric to a line if the line is the perpendicular bisector of the segment joining the points. The line is called the *axis of symmetry* of the two given points. Thus the points (4,3) and (−4,3) are symmetric with respect to the *y*-axis.

Further, in the parabola whose equation is $x^2 = 4y$, $x = \pm 2\sqrt{y}$. Hence, for each positive value of y, there correspond two values of x, and it is seen that the graph consists entirely of pairs of points which are symmetric with respect to the *y*-axis.

In general, if the substitution of $-x$ for x leaves the equation unchanged, the graph of the equation is symmetric with respect to the *y*-axis.

Similarly, if the substitution of $-y$ for y leaves the equation unchanged, the graph of the equation is symmetric with respect to the *x*-axis.

Also, two points are said to be symmetric with respect to a third point if the third point is the bisector of the line segment joining the points. Thus, the points (4,5) and (−4,−5) are symmetric with respect to the origin.

Hence, it follows that, if the simultaneous substitution of $-x$ for x and $-y$ for y leaves the equation unchanged, the graph of the equation is symmetric with respect to the origin.

EXAMPLE. Examine the equation, $x^2y - 4 = 0$, for symmetry, with respect to the coordinate axes and the origin.

The substitution of $-x$ for x gives $(-x)^2y - 4 = 0$, which reduces to $x^2y - 4 = 0$, leaving the equation unchanged. Therefore the graph of the equation is symmetric with respect to the *y*-axis.

However, the substitution of $-y$ for y gives $x^2(-y) - 4 = 0$ or $-x^2y - 4 = 0$, changing the original equation. Therefore the graph is *not* symmetric with respect to the *x*-axis.

Similarly, it can be shown that the graph is not symmetric

Curve Tracing / 71

with respect to the origin, since the simultaneous substitution of $-x$ for x and $-y$ for y changes the equation.

E X E R C I S E S

Test the following equations for symmetry with respect to the axes and the origin:

1. $x^2 + y^2 - 36 = 0$.
2. $x^2 - y^2 - 9 = 0$.
3. $xy - 10 = 0$.
4. $x^4 + y^4 - 1 = 0$.
5. $x^2 + y^2 - 2xy - 9 = 0$.
6. $x^2 y^3 - 10 = 0$.
7. $x^2 y - 3y - y^2 - 10 = 0$.
8. $x^3 + 2x - 3y - 7 = 0$.
9. $5x^2 - 3xy + 3y^2 - 6 = 0$.
10. $x^4 - x^2 y - 4 = 0$.

(b) *Intercepts.* The intercepts a graph, as previously noted, are the distances from the origin to the points where the graph crosses the axes. Accordingly, to find the x-intercept, set $y = 0$ in the given equation and solve for x; to find the y-intercept, set $x = 0$ in the equation and solve for y.

(c) *Range and Domain.* These properties of the graph of an equation are best illustrated by the following example.

EXAMPLE 1. Find the range and the domain of the graph of $x^4 + y^4 = 1$.

(1) Solve for y:　　$y = \pm \sqrt[4]{1 - x^4}$.

Since y can have real values only when $|x| \leq 1$, then the domain of the graph is given by $-1 \leq x \leq 1$.

(2) Solve for x:　　$x = \pm \sqrt[4]{1 - y^4}$.

Since x can have real values only when $|y| \leq 1$, then the range is given by $-1 \leq y \leq 1$.

(d) *Asymptotes.* As noted in Chapter 4 in connection with the discussion of the hyperbola, an asymptote to a curve is the straight line to which the curve gets closer and closer but never reaches.

The method of finding the asymptotes is illustrated by the following example.

72 / Curve Tracing

EXAMPLE 2. Find the asymptotes, if any exist, of

$$x^2y + 2x - y - 5 = 0.$$

(1) Solve for y: $y = \dfrac{5 - 2x}{x^2 - 1}.$

As $|x|$ approaches 1, $x^2 - 1$ approaches 0 as a limit and y increases without limit. Therefore the lines $x - 1 = 0$ and $x + 1 = 0$ are asymptotes to the curve.

(2) Now, solve the given equation for x. Here, the "quadratic formula" is employed, giving

$$x = \frac{-1 \pm \sqrt{y^2 + 5y + 1}}{y}.$$

Therefore, the line $y = 0$ (the x-axis) is an asymptote.

A knowledge of the symmetry, the intercepts, the range and domain, and the asymptotes of the graph, together with the co-ordinates of a few selected points which satisfy the equation of the graph, furnish sufficient data to make a satisfactory sketch of the graph.

EXAMPLE 3. Examine the equation

$$x^2y + x^2 - 4y - 16 = 0,$$

and sketch its graph.

(a) *Symmetry.* Since the substitution of $-x$ for x leaves the equation unchanged, the graph is symmetric with respect to the y-axis. The substitution of $-y$ for y changes the equation. Hence, the graph is symmetric to neither the x-axis nor the origin.

(b) *Intercepts.* If $y = 0$, the equation becomes $x^2 - 16 = 0$. Hence $x = \pm 4$ and the x-intercepts are $x = 4$ and $x = -4$. If $x = 0$, the equation becomes $-4y - 16 = 0$. Hence $y = -4$ and the y-intercept is $y = -4$.

(c) *Domain and Range.* Solve the equation for y:

$$y = \frac{16 - x^2}{x^2 - 4}.$$

Therefore the domain is all the real values of x, except $x = 2$ and $x = -2$.

Solve the equation for x:

$$x = \pm 2 \sqrt{\frac{y + 4}{y + 1}}$$

and hence x is *real* if either (1) the numerator and the denominator are both positive, which is true when $y > -1$, or (2) the numerator and the denominator are both negative, which is true when $y \leq -4$.

Therefore the range is all the real values of y, *except* where $-4 < y \leq -1$.

(d) *Asymptotes*. From the equation for y which is given above,

$$y = \frac{16 - x^2}{x^2 - 4},$$

it is seen that the asymptotes are the lines $x + 2 = 0$ and $x - 2 = 0$.

Also, from

$$x = \pm 2 \sqrt{\frac{y + 4}{y + 1}},$$

it is seen that the line $y + 1 = 0$ is an asymptote.

A short table of corresponding values of x and y may be constructed, as follows:

x	$\pm\frac{1}{2}$	± 1	± 3	± 4	± 5
y	$-4\frac{1}{5}$	-5	$1\frac{2}{5}$	0	$-\frac{3}{7}$

When all of the above data are considered, the following graph can be sketched (Fig. 5-10):

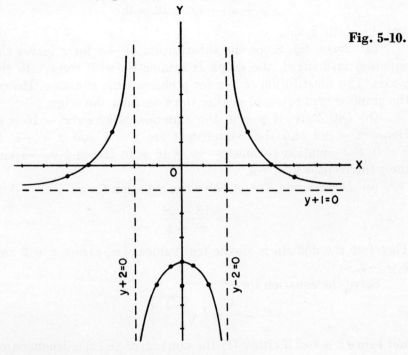

Fig. 5-10.

E X E R C I S E S

Sketch the graphs of the following equations:

1. $x^2y - 4 = 0$.
2. $xy + 2x - y - 5 = 0$.
3. $x^2y + 3x^2 - 4y - 24 = 0$.
4. $xy^2 - 9 = 0$.
5. $6xy + 8x - 3y - 2 = 0$.
6. $x^2y - 2x^2 - 9y + 12 = 0$.
7. $xy - 3x + 2y - 7 = 0$.
8. $xy - x + 2y - 8 = 0$.
9. $x^2y + 2x - y - 5 = 0$.
10. $x^2y - x - 5 = 0$.

6

POLAR COORDINATES

6-1 Polar Coordinates

In the Cartesian system, a point is located in a plane by two numbers, which are the rectangular coordinates of the point. By the proper choice of axes, it is often possible to simplify the work of finding the equation of the locus under consideration. However, for certain loci, it is desirable to employ a different system for locating points in a plane, namely, the system of *polar coordinates*. In this system, the point is located by giving its direction and its distance from a fixed point, called the *pole*.

Let O (Fig. 6-1) be the pole and let the line OA, in a given direction through O, be the *polar axis* of this system.

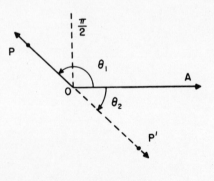

Fig. 6-1.

The straight line through O perpendicular to the polar axis is the $\frac{\pi}{2}$-axis.

Accordingly, the point P is determined if its distance ρ from the pole, O, and the angle θ, which the line OP makes with the polar axis, OA, are given.

The distance ρ is called the *radius vector* and the angle θ is called the *vectorial angle*.

Although the radius vector is usually written first, such as $P(\rho,\theta)$, in practice, the vectorial angle is constructed first, and the radius vector is marked off on the terminal side of the angle. The polar axis is always considered the initial side of the angle.

The vectorial angle is positive if it is measured counter-clockwise from the polar axis and negative if it is measured clock-wise from the polar axis. Thus, in Fig. 6-1, θ_1 is positive and θ_2 is negative.

Also, ρ is positive if P is located on the terminal side of angle θ and negative if P is located on the terminal side of angle θ, produced through the pole, O.

Thus, it is seen that, for every pair of real numbers (ρ,θ), there is one point on the plane. However, for every point on the plane there is an infinity of pairs of polar coordinates, since ρ and θ may both be positive, both be negative or one positive and the other negative, and also θ has an infinity of equivalent co-terminal angles of the form $\theta + 2\pi n$, where n is any integer.

EXAMPLE 1. Plot the point $\left(3, \frac{\pi}{6}\right)$.

Sketch the angle $AOP = \frac{\pi}{6}$ and lay off $OP = 3$ units, as in Fig. 6-2.

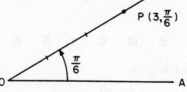

P $\left(3, \frac{\pi}{6}\right)$

$\frac{\pi}{6}$

O — A

Fig. 6-2.

EXAMPLE 2. Plot the point $\left(2, -\frac{3\pi}{4}\right)$.

Sketch the angle $AOP = -\frac{3\pi}{4}$ and lay off $OP = 2$ units, as in Fig. 6-3.

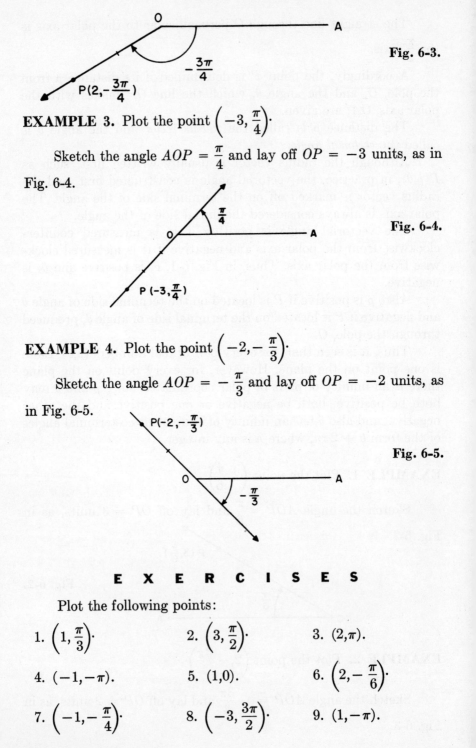

Fig. 6-3.

EXAMPLE 3. Plot the point $\left(-3, \dfrac{\pi}{4}\right)$.

Sketch the angle $AOP = \dfrac{\pi}{4}$ and lay off $OP = -3$ units, as in Fig. 6-4.

Fig. 6-4.

EXAMPLE 4. Plot the point $\left(-2, -\dfrac{\pi}{3}\right)$.

Sketch the angle $AOP = -\dfrac{\pi}{3}$ and lay off $OP = -2$ units, as in Fig. 6-5.

Fig. 6-5.

E X E R C I S E S

Plot the following points:

1. $\left(1, \dfrac{\pi}{3}\right)$.

2. $\left(3, \dfrac{\pi}{2}\right)$.

3. $(2, \pi)$.

4. $(-1, -\pi)$.

5. $(1, 0)$.

6. $\left(2, -\dfrac{\pi}{6}\right)$.

7. $\left(-1, -\dfrac{\pi}{4}\right)$.

8. $\left(-3, \dfrac{3\pi}{2}\right)$.

9. $(1, -\pi)$.

10. $\left(-2, -\dfrac{3\pi}{2}\right)$.   11. $(3, 9\pi)$.   12. $(-5, -\pi)$.

13. $(-1, \pi)$.   14. $\left(-1, \dfrac{\pi}{2}\right)$.   15. $(3, -3\pi)$.

6-2 *Relation Between Rectangular Coordinates and Polar Coordinates*

Place a polar system of coordinates upon a rectangular system so that the pole falls upon the origin and the polar axis falls along the positive direction of the x-axis.

Then, as in Fig. 6-6, the rectangular coordinates of a point P are (x, y) and the polar coordinates are (ρ, θ).

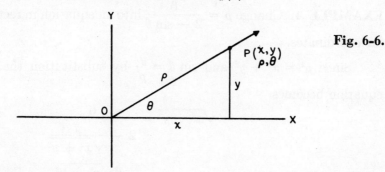

Fig. 6-6.

From the above figure, it follows that $x = \rho \cos \theta$ and $y = \rho \sin \theta$ or $\rho = \sqrt{x^2 + y^2}$ and $\tan \theta = \dfrac{y}{x}$, or $\theta = \text{arc} \tan \dfrac{y}{x}$.

The use of these formulas is illustrated in the following examples:

EXAMPLE 1. Change $P(3, 3)$ to polar coordinates.

$$\theta = \text{arc} \tan \frac{3}{3} = \text{arc} \tan 1 = \frac{\pi}{4},$$

$$\rho = \sqrt{9 + 9} = \sqrt{18} = 3\sqrt{2}.$$

Therefore the polar coordinates of P are $\left(3\sqrt{2}, \dfrac{\pi}{4}\right)$.

EXAMPLE 2. Change $P\left(2, \dfrac{\pi}{3}\right)$ to rectangular coordinates.

$$x = 2 \cos \frac{\pi}{3} = 2\left(\frac{1}{2}\right) = 1,$$

$$y = 2 \sin \frac{\pi}{3} = 2\left(\frac{1}{2}\sqrt{3}\right) = \sqrt{3}.$$

Therefore the rectangular coordinates of P are $(1, \sqrt{3})$.

EXAMPLE 3. Change the equation of the ellipse $b^2x^2 + a^2y^2 - a^2b^2 = 0$ into an equation in polar coordinates.

Since $x^2 = \rho^2 \cos^2 \theta$ and $y^2 = \rho^2 \sin^2 \theta$, by substitution,

$$\rho^2 b^2 \cos^2 \theta + \rho^2 a^2 \sin^2 \theta = a^2 b^2$$
$$\rho^2(b^2 \cos^2 \theta + a^2 \sin^2 \theta) = a^2 b^2,$$

and
$$\rho^2 = \frac{a^2 b^2}{b^2 \cos^2 \theta + a^2 \sin^2 \theta}$$

is the required equation in polar coordinates.

EXAMPLE 4. Change $\rho = \dfrac{6}{2 - \sin \theta}$ into an equation in rectangular coordinates.

Since $\rho^2 = x^2 + y^2$ and $\sin \theta = \dfrac{y}{\rho}$, by substitution the given equation becomes

$$\sqrt{x^2 + y^2} = \frac{6}{2 - \dfrac{y}{\sqrt{x^2 + y^2}}}$$

$$= \frac{6\sqrt{x^2 + y^2}}{2\sqrt{x^2 + y^2} - y}.$$

Divide both sides by $\sqrt{x^2 + y^2}$:

Therefore,
$$1 = \frac{6}{2\sqrt{x^2 + y^2} - y}$$

and
$$2\sqrt{x^2 + y^2} - y = 6.$$

Square:
$$4x^2 + 4y^2 = 36 + 12y + y^2$$

or
$$4x^2 + 3y^2 - 12y - 36 = 0.$$

This is recognized as the equation of an ellipse in rectangular coordinates.

E X E R C I S E S

Change to polar coordinates:

1. $(1,1)$.

2. $(2,-2)$.

3. $(-1,\sqrt{3})$.

4. $(0,2)$.

5. $(-1,0)$.

6. $(5\sqrt{3},-5)$.

Change to rectangular coordinates:

7. $\left(2, \dfrac{\pi}{4}\right)$.

10. $(3,0)$.

8. $(-1,\pi)$.

11. $\left(-6, -\dfrac{\pi}{4}\right)$.

9. $\left(\sqrt{2}, \dfrac{3\pi}{4}\right)$.

12. $\left(-16, \dfrac{\pi}{6}\right)$.

Transform the following polar equations into equations in rectangular coordinates:

13. $5 \cos \theta = 4$.

16. $\rho = \dfrac{4}{1 - 2 \cos \theta}$.

14. $\rho = 8$.

17. $\rho = 8 \sin \theta$.

15. $\rho = \dfrac{4}{3 - \cos \theta}$.

18. $\rho = 8 \cos \theta$.

Transform the following rectangular equations into equations in polar coordinates:

19. $y = 4x$.

22. $x^2 - y^2 = 1$.

20. $xy = 9$.

23. $4x^2 - 9y^2 = 36$.

21. $x^2 + y^2 = 16$.

24. $x^2 + y^2 - 10y = 0$.

6-3 Simple Polar Equations

It is desirable to be able to recognize at sight the loci of certain simple equations, expressed in polar coordinates, as follows:

STRAIGHT LINES

EXAMPLE 1. $\theta = k$.

Let l, be a straight line through the pole, O, whose vectorial angle is k, as in Fig. 6-7.

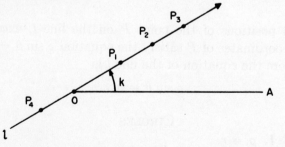

Fig. 6-7.

The coordinates of all the points P_1, P_2, P_3, P_4 etc., which lie on the line l, satisfy the equation $\theta = k$.

Therefore the equation of the line is

$$\theta = k.$$

EXAMPLE 2. $\rho \cos \theta = a$.

Let l be a straight line perpendicular to the polar axis, OA, and at a distance a from the pole, O. Also, let $P(\rho,\theta)$ be any point on the line l, as in Fig. 6-8.

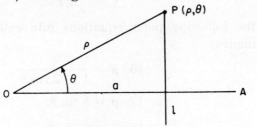

Fig. 6-8.

For all positions of the point P on the line l, except where $\theta = \frac{\pi}{2}$, the coordinates of P satisfy the equation $\rho \cos \theta = a$.

Therefore the equation of the line l is

$$\rho \cos \theta = a.$$

EXAMPLE 3. $\rho \sin \theta = a$.

Let l be a straight line parallel to the polar axis, OA, and at a distance a from the pole, O. Also, let $P(\rho,\theta)$ be any point of the line l, as in Fig. 6-9.

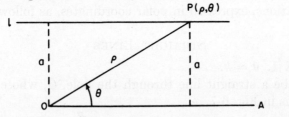

Fig. 6-9.

For all positions of the point P on the line l, except where $\theta = 0$, the coordinates of P satisfy the equation $\rho \sin \theta = a$.

Therefore the equation of the line l is

$$\rho \sin \theta = a.$$

CIRCLES

EXAMPLE 1. $\rho = r$.

Let the point $P(\rho,\theta)$ be any point on the circle whose center is at the pole O and whose radius is r, as in Fig. 6-10.

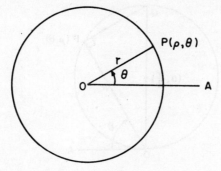

Fig. 6-10.

For all positions of the point P on the circle, the coordinates of P satisfy the equation $\rho = r$.

Therefore, the equation of the circle is

$$\rho = r.$$

EXAMPLE 2. $\rho = 2a \cos \theta$.

Let $P(\rho,\theta)$ be any point on the circle whose center is at the point (a,O) and whose radius is a, as in Fig. 6-11.

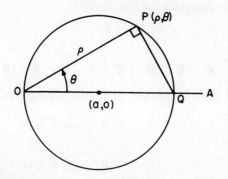

Fig. 6-11.

For all positions of point P on the circle, angle OPQ is a right angle, since it is inscribed in a semicircle. Therefore, in the right triangle OPQ,

$$\overline{OP} = \overline{OQ} \cos QOP,$$
or
$$\rho = 2a \cos \theta.$$

Therefore, the equation of this circle is

$$\rho = 2a \cos \theta.$$

EXAMPLE 3. $\rho = 2a \sin \theta$.

Let $P(\rho,\theta)$ be any point on the circle whose center is at the point $\left(a, \dfrac{\pi}{2}\right)$ and whose radius is a, as in Fig. 6-12.

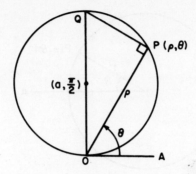

Fig. 6-12.

For all positions of point P on the circle, angle OPQ is a right angle, since it is inscribed in a semicircle. Therefore, in the right triangle OPQ,

$$\overline{OP} = \overline{OQ} \cos POQ,$$

or
$$\rho = 2a \cos\left(\frac{\pi}{2} - \theta\right)$$

or
$$\rho = 2a \sin \theta.$$

Therefore the equation of the circle is

$$\rho = 2a \sin \theta.$$

E X E R C I S E S

Identify and sketch the loci of the following equations:

1. $\theta = \dfrac{\pi}{4}.$
2. $\theta = \dfrac{5\pi}{6}.$
3. $\rho = 3.$
4. $\rho = -1.$
5. $\rho \cos \theta = 3.$
6. $\rho \sin \theta = 4.$
7. $\rho = 6 \sin \theta.$
8. $\rho = -8 \cos \theta.$

6-4 Sketching Loci of Equations in Polar Coordinates

As is the case with equations in rectangular coordinates, any equation in ρ and θ represents a curve that is the locus of all points whose coordinates (ρ, θ) satisfy the given equation.

Accordingly, to find the locus of a given equation in polar coordinates it is best to solve the equation for ρ in terms of θ, assign convenient values to θ, obtain corresponding values for ρ, and construct a table of these values. Then, these corresponding values of ρ and θ are plotted and a smooth curve is drawn connecting these points.

EXAMPLE. Sketch the locus of $\rho = 1 + \cos \theta$.

Construct a table of corresponding values of ρ and θ, as follows:

θ	0	$\pm \dfrac{\pi}{6}$	$\pm \dfrac{\pi}{4}$	$\pm \dfrac{\pi}{3}$	$\pm \dfrac{\pi}{2}$	$\pm \dfrac{2\pi}{3}$	$\pm \dfrac{3\pi}{4}$	$\pm \dfrac{5\pi}{6}$	$\pm\pi$
ρ	2	1.9	1.7	1.5	1	0.5	0.3	0.1	0

The graph of the curve determined by these points is seen in Fig. 6-13.

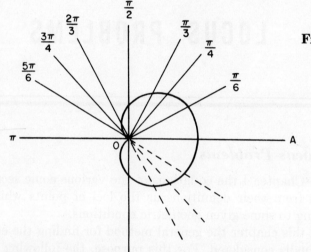

Fig. 6-13.

E X E R C I S E S

Sketch the loci of the following equations:

1. $\rho = 1 - \cos \theta$.

2. $\rho = 1 + \sin \theta$.

3. $\rho = 10 \sin 2\theta$.

4. $\rho = 10 \cos 2\theta$.

5. $\rho = 10 \sin 3\theta$.

6. $\rho = 10 \cos 3\theta$.

7. $\rho = \dfrac{12}{2 - \cos \theta}$.

8. $\rho = \dfrac{8}{1 + 3 \sin \theta}$.

9. $\rho = \theta$.

10. $\rho\theta = 4$.

7

LOCUS PROBLEMS

7-1 Locus Problems

In Chapter 4 the equations of the various conic sections were derived from their definitions as the loci of points which moved according to some given geometric conditions.

In this chapter the general method for finding the equation of any locus is considered. For this purpose, the following procedure is suggested:

(a) Choose the origin and the axes in a convenient position.
(b) Designate by $P(x,y)$ a point which satisfies the given geometric condition.
(c) Draw any lines that are suggested by the given data.
(d) Express in algebraic language the given geometric condition.
(e) Simplify the resulting algebraic equation involving the coordinates x and y and the given constants.

This procedure is best illustrated by the following examples:

EXAMPLE 1. Find the equation of the locus of a point which moves so that its distance from the point $(-8,0)$ is twice its distance from the point $(4,0)$. Describe the locus and sketch it.

Let $P(x,y)$ be any point which satisfies the given condition, where $Q(-8,0)$ and $P(4,0)$ are the given points (Fig. 7-1).

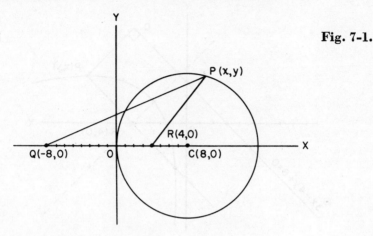

Fig. 7-1.

From the given condition,

$$PQ = 2PR.$$

But $$PQ = \sqrt{(x + 8)^2 + y^2}$$
and $$PR = \sqrt{(x - 4)^2 + y^2}.$$
Therefore, $$\sqrt{(x + 8)^2 + y^2} = 2\sqrt{(x - 4)^2 + y^2}.$$

Square both sides:

$$x^2 + 16x + 64 + y^2 = 4x^2 - 32x + 64 + 4y^2.$$
Simplify: $$3x^2 + 3y^2 - 48x = 0$$
and $$x^2 + y^2 - 16x = 0.$$

Complete the square and balance:

$$(x^2 - 16x + 64) + y^2 = 64$$
or $$(x - 8)^2 + y^2 = 64.$$

This is the equation of a circle whose center is at the point $(8,0)$ and whose radius equals 8.

EXAMPLE 2. Find the equation of the locus of a point which moves so that it is always equidistant from the point $(4,0)$ and the line $3x - 4y + 8 = 0$.

By definition (see Section 4-8), this locus is a parabola. Because the directrix is not parallel to an axis, the curve is rotated and its equation contains an xy term.

Although the sketching of a "rotated" parabola is beyond the scope of this text, the equation can be found as follows:

Let $P(x,y)$ be any point which satisfies the given conditions, as in Fig. 7-2.

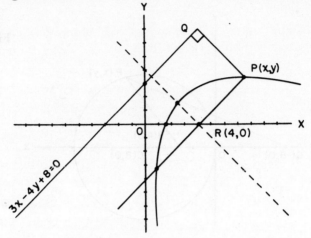

Fig. 7-2.

From the given condition,

$$PR = PQ.$$

But

$$PR = \sqrt{(x-4)^2 + y^2}$$

and

$$PQ = \frac{3x - 4y + 8}{5}$$

(Section 3-10).

Therefore,

$$\sqrt{(x-4)^2 + y^2} = \frac{3x - 4y + 8}{5}.$$

Square both sides, clear of fractions, and simplify, to get

$$16x^2 + 24xy + 9y^2 - 248x + 64y + 336 = 0.$$

This is the required equation.

E X E R C I S E S

1. Find the equation of the locus of a point which moves so that it is always equidistant from the points $(7,-2)$ and $(1,4)$.

2. Find the equation of the locus of a point which moves so that it is equidistant from the points $(-3,6)$ and $(5,-2)$.

3. Find the equation of the locus of a point which moves so that its distance from the point $(-2,0)$ is one-half its distance from the point $(4,0)$.

4. Find the equation of the locus of a point which moves so that its distance from the point $(-1,-4)$ is two-thirds its distance from the point $(7,2)$.

5. Find the equation of the perpendicular bisector of the line segment joining the points $(-4,3)$ and $(6,-2)$, using the concept of locus.

6. Find the equation of the perpendicular bisector of the line segment joining the points $(5,-1)$ and $(-3,7)$, using the concept of locus.

7. Find the equation of the locus of a point which moves so that the sum of its distances from the points $(0,4)$ and $(0,-4)$ is equal to 10.

8. Find the equation of the locus of a point which moves so that the sum of its distances from the points $(3,3)$ and $(-3,3)$ is equal to 10.

9. Find the equation of the locus of a point which moves so that the difference of its distances from the points $(5,0)$ and $(-5,0)$ is equal to 6.

10. Find the equation of the locus of points whose ordinates are one-half the ordinates of $x^2 + y^2 - 16 = 0$.

11. Find the equation of the locus of a point which moves so that it is always equidistant from the point $(4,2)$ and from the line $x - y = 0$.

12. Find the equation of the locus of a point whose ordinate is a mean proportional between its distances from the lines $x - y = 0$ and $x + y = 0$.

8

THE DERIVATIVE

8-1 Introduction

Sir Isaac Newton (1642–1727) and Gottfried Wilhelm Leibnitz (1646–1716) are believed to have invented the calculus, independently and simultaneously, in the latter part of the 17th Century.

The calculus is a very powerful tool which is used for finding the solutions to many scientific and engineering problems. It is also fundamental for the study of higher mathematics.

The following examples are suggestive of the type of problems which are easily solved by the methods of the calculus:

(a) A piece of sheet metal 18 inches by 12 inches is to be made into an open box by cutting out squares from the corners and bending up the flaps, as in Fig. 8-1. What is the size of the side of the cut-out square so that the volume of the box is a maximum?

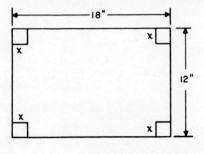

Fig. 8-1.

(b) A ladder which is 20 feet long is leaning against a wall. The bottom of the ladder is moving away from the wall at the rate of 2 feet per second. At what rate is the top of the ladder moving down the wall, when the bottom of the ladder is 10 feet from the wall?

(c) Find the area inside the parabola $y = x^2$ to a depth of 4 units.

Examples (a) and (b) are problems in *differential calculus*, while example (c) is a problem in *integral calculus*.

8-2 Limits

As the concept of *limits* is fundamental to the study of calculus, certain definitions are given and certain basic concepts are illustrated in the following examples:

EXAMPLE 1. If $f(x) = 3x + 1$, what is the limit of $f(x)$ as x approaches 2?

This is written

$$\lim_{x \to 2} f(x)$$

and is read, "the limit of $f(x)$ as x approaches 2."

Values of $f(x)$ which correspond to values of x, which are different from, but in the neighborhood of, 2, are listed in the following tables:

x	1.8	1.9	1.95	1.99	1.995	...
$f(x)$	6.4	6.7	6.85	6.97	6.985	...

x	2.2	2.1	2.05	2.01	2.005	...
$f(x)$	7.6	7.3	7.15	7.03	7.015	...

Thus it is seen that, as x approaches 2, $f(x)$ approaches 7, i.e.,

$$\lim_{x \to 2} f(x) = 7.$$

But $f(2) = 3(2) + 1 = 7$.

Therefore

$$\lim_{x \to 2} f(x) = f(2).$$

In general, if $f(a)$ exists at a and in the neighborhood of a, then

$$\lim_{x \to a} f(x) = f(a).$$

For the finding of limiting values of functions, the following three theorems on limits are of fundamental importance.

If $u = f_1(x)$, $v = f_2(x)$, and $w = f_3(x)$ and $\lim_{x \to a} u = L_1$, $\lim_{x \to a} v = L_2$, and $\lim_{x \to a} w = L_3$, then:

(a) $\lim_{x \to a} (u + v + w) = L_1 + L_2 + L_3$;

(b) $\lim_{x \to a} (uvw) = L_1 L_2 L_3$;

(c) $\lim_{x \to a} \dfrac{u}{v} = \dfrac{L_1}{L_2}$, provided $L_2 \neq 0$.

These three theorems, whose proof is beyond the scope of this text, may be stated in words as follows:

(a) The limit of a sum is the sum of the limits.
(b) The limit of a product is the product of the limits.
(c) The limit of a quotient is the quotient of the limits, provided that the denominator is not zero.

EXAMPLE 2. If $f(x) = x^2 - 3x + 2$, find $\lim_{x \to 4} f(x)$.

Applying Theorem (a),
$$\lim_{x \to 4} f(x) = \lim_{x \to 4} x^2 + \lim_{x \to 4} (-3x) + \lim_{x \to 4} 2$$
$$= 16 - 12 + 2 = 6.$$

EXAMPLE 3. Find $\lim_{x \to 3} \left(\dfrac{x + 1}{x - 2} \right)$.

Applying Theorem (c),
$$\lim_{x \to 3} \left(\frac{x + 1}{x - 2} \right) = \frac{\lim_{x \to 3} (x + 1)}{\lim_{x \to 3} (x - 2)} = \frac{4}{1} = 4.$$

If $f(x)$ does not exist at $x = a$, then the procedure for finding the limit of $f(x)$ as x approaches a—if a finite limit does exist—is illustrated by the following examples:

EXAMPLE 4. Find the limit of the sum S of the infinite geometric series $\dfrac{1}{2} + \dfrac{1}{4} + \dfrac{1}{8} + \dfrac{1}{16} + \dfrac{1}{32} + \dfrac{1}{64} + \cdots + \dfrac{1}{2^n} + \cdots$.

We can compute:
$$\frac{1}{2} + \frac{1}{4} = \frac{3}{4},$$

$$\frac{1}{2} + \frac{1}{4} + \frac{1}{8} = \frac{7}{8},$$

$$\frac{1}{2} + \frac{1}{4} + \frac{1}{8} + \frac{1}{16} = \frac{15}{16},$$

$$\frac{1}{2} + \frac{1}{4} + \frac{1}{8} + \frac{1}{16} + \frac{1}{32} = \frac{31}{32},$$

$$\frac{1}{2} + \frac{1}{4} + \frac{1}{8} + \frac{1}{16} + \frac{1}{32} + \frac{1}{64} = \frac{63}{64}.$$

Also,

$$\frac{1}{2} + \frac{1}{4} + \frac{1}{8} + \frac{1}{16} + \frac{1}{32} + \cdots + \frac{1}{2^n} = \frac{2^n - 1}{2^n} = 1 - \frac{1}{2^n}.$$

Thus, as n increases without limit, the value of $\frac{1}{2^n}$ approaches 0 and $\left(1 - \frac{1}{2^n}\right)$ approaches 1. However, the sum of these n terms is never 1, even though the limit is exactly 1.

The sum of the first six terms of the series differs from 1 by $\frac{1}{64}$, which is less than 0.02, and the sum of the first seven terms differs from 1 by $\frac{1}{128}$, which is less than 0.01, etc. Thus, as n increases without limit, the value of S differs from the limit 1 by a smaller and smaller amount.

This condition is expressed by writing

$$\lim_{n \to \infty} S = 1.$$

This is read: "the limit, as n increases without limit, of the sum S of the given series is 1.

EXAMPLE 5. If $f(x) = \left(\frac{1}{3}\right)^{\frac{1}{x^2}}$, find $\lim_{x \to 0} f(x)$.

Here, $f(0)$ has no meaning, since the replacement of x by 0 makes the exponent $\frac{1}{x^2}$ equal to $\frac{1}{0}$, which does not exist. Accordingly, the following table is constructed, where $\left(\frac{1}{3}\right)^{\frac{1}{x^2}}$ is equal to $\frac{1}{3^{\frac{1}{x^2}}}$

x	± 1	$\pm \dfrac{1}{2}$	$\pm \dfrac{1}{3}$	$\cdots$	$\pm \dfrac{1}{n}$
$f(x)$	$\dfrac{1}{3}$	$\dfrac{1}{81}$	$\dfrac{1}{20683}$	$\cdots$	$\dfrac{1}{3^{n^2}}$

As x approaches 0, $\dfrac{1}{x^2}$ increases without limit and therefore the denominator $3^{\frac{1}{x^2}}$ increases without limit. Consequently, the fraction $\dfrac{1}{3^{\frac{1}{x^2}}}$ decreases toward 0.

Hence, $$\lim_{x \to 0}\left[\left(\frac{1}{3}\right)^{\frac{1}{x^2}}\right] = 0.$$

EXAMPLE 6. If $f(x) = \dfrac{x^2 - 4}{x - 2}$, find $\lim\limits_{x \to 2} f(x)$.

Here, $f(x)$ does not exist at $x = 2$, since the denominator becomes 0 and division by 0 is impossible.

However, if $x \neq 2$, but is in the neighborhood of 2, then $x^2 - 4$ can be divided by $x - 2$ and
$$f(x) = x + 2.$$
Since $$\lim_{x \to 2} (x + 2) = 4,$$

therefore, $$\lim_{x \to 2} \frac{x^2 - 4}{x - 2} = 4.$$

The truth of this conclusion can also be seen from the following table:

x	1	1.5	1.75	1.9	. . .
$f(x)$	3	3.5	3.75	3.9	. . .

x	3	2.5	2.25	2.1	. . .
$f(x)$	5	4.5	4.25	4.1	. . . .

Therefore, as x approaches 2 (from either side), $f(x)$ differs from 4 by a smaller and a smaller number.

These last three examples (4, 5, and 6) lead to the following generalized statement:

The value of a function $f(x)$ approaches a constant L as a limit, if, as x approaches a, the values of the function are such that $|f(x) - L|$ becomes and remains less than any pre-assigned positive number however small.

This is written
$$\lim_{x \to a} f(x) = L.$$

Find the following limits:

1. $\lim\limits_{x \to 3} (x^3 - 2x - 4)$.

2. $\lim\limits_{x \to 5} \left(\dfrac{x + 1}{x - 3} \right)$.

3. $\lim\limits_{x \to 3} \left(\dfrac{x^2 + 3x}{2x + 3} \right)$.

4. $\lim\limits_{x \to 1} \left(\dfrac{3}{2 + x} \right)$.

5. $\lim\limits_{x \to 0} \left(\dfrac{3x^2 + 6x}{x} \right)$.

6. $\lim\limits_{x \to 3} \left(\dfrac{x^2 - 9}{x - 3} \right)$.

7. $\lim\limits_{x \to -1} \left(\dfrac{x^2 - 1}{x + 1} \right)$.

8. $\lim\limits_{x \to 2} \left(\dfrac{x^3 - 8}{x - 2} \right)$.

9. $\lim\limits_{x \to 5} \left(\dfrac{x^2 - 4x - 5}{x - 5} \right)$.

10. $\lim\limits_{x \to 2} \left(\dfrac{x^4 - 16}{x - 2} \right)$.

11. $\lim\limits_{h \to 0} \left[\dfrac{(3 + h)^2 - 9}{h} \right]$.

12. $\lim\limits_{x \to 0} \left[\left(\dfrac{1}{2} \right)^{\frac{1}{x^2}} \right]$.

8-3 Continuous Functions

A function $y = f(x)$ is *continuous* at $x = c$, if c is in the domain of the function and if

$$\lim_{x \to c} f(x) = f(c).$$

A function which does not satisfy this condition is *discontinuous* at $x = c$.

A function which is continuous at every point in the interval $a \le x \le b$ is *continuous in that interval*.

For example, the function which is defined by the equation $f(x) = x^2$ and whose graph is a parabola (Fig. 8-2) satisfies the condition for continuity.

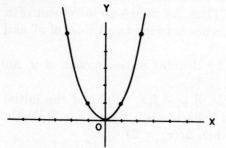

Fig. 8-2.

Since $f(c) = c^2$ and $\lim\limits_{x \to c} f(x) = c^2$, and the domain of $f(x)$ is all the real numbers, then $f(x)$ is continuous everywhere.

However, the function which is defined by the equation $f(x) = \dfrac{10}{x}$ and whose graph is an equilateral hyperbola (Fig. 8-3) is discontinuous at $x = 0$, since this value of x does not lie in the domain of the function.

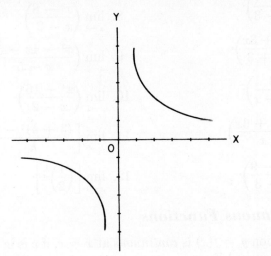

Fig. 8-3.

8-4 Increments

An *increment* of a variable is the amount by which the variable changes between two of its numerical values. The increment is found by subtracting the initial value of the variable from the terminal value of the variable. Accordingly, the increment may be positive or negative according as the variable is increasing or decreasing.

An increment is usually denoted by the Greek letter Δ, which is read "delta." Thus, Δx means an increment of x. The symbol Δx means "the difference between two values of x" and not the product of Δ by x.

Similarly, Δy denotes an increment of y, and $\Delta f(x)$ denotes an increment of $f(x)$.

For example, if $y = f(x) = x^2$ and the initial value of x is 2 and the terminal value of x is 5, then $\Delta x = 3$. Further, since $f(2) = 4$ and $f(5) = 25$, then $\Delta f(x) = 21$.

In general, curves are analyzed as x increases in value, so Δx is generally positive. However, Δy may be either positive or negative, depending upon whether y is increasing or decreasing as x increases.

8-5 Slope of a Curve

The *slope of a curve* at a given point is the slope of the tangent to the curve at that point.

For example, let $P(x,y)$ be a given point on the curve $y = f(x)$ and let Q be any neighboring point whose coordinates are $(x + \Delta x, y + \Delta y)$, as in Fig. 8-4.

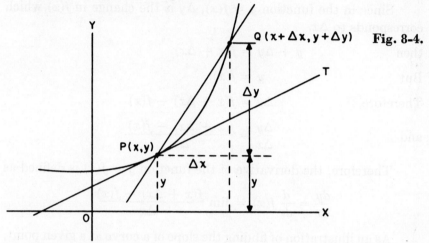

Fig. 8-4.

From the figure it is seen that the slope of the secant PQ is $\dfrac{\Delta y}{\Delta x}$.

Now let Q move along the curve, approaching the point P as a limiting position. The secant then revolves around P, with the tangent PT as its limiting position.

The increment Δx approaches 0 as a limit, and so does the increment Δy.

Then the limit of $\dfrac{\Delta y}{\Delta x}$, as $\Delta x \to 0$, represents the slope of the tangent PT.

This limit of $\dfrac{\Delta y}{\Delta x}$, as $\Delta x \to 0$ is called the *derivative of y with respect to x*, and is denoted by the symbol $\dfrac{dy}{dx}$.

Therefore,
$$\frac{dy}{dx} = \lim_{\Delta x \to 0} \frac{\Delta y}{\Delta x}.$$

The symbol $\dfrac{dy}{dx}$ must *not* be considered as a fraction, but simply as a notation for the *limit of a ratio*.

This symbol may be interpreted as

$$\frac{dy}{dx} = \frac{d}{dx}(y),$$

where $\frac{d}{dx}$ denotes the operation "the derivative with respect to x."

Since in the function $y = f(x)$, Δy is the change in $f(x)$ which corresponds to Δx,

then $\qquad\qquad y + \Delta y = f(x + \Delta x).$

But $\qquad\qquad y = f(x).$

Therefore, $\qquad \Delta y = f(x + \Delta x) - f(x)$

and $\qquad\qquad \dfrac{\Delta y}{\Delta x} = \dfrac{f(x + \Delta x) - f(x)}{\Delta x}.$

Therefore, the derivative of the function $y = f(x)$ is defined as

$$\frac{dy}{dx} = \frac{d}{dx}f(x) = \lim_{\Delta x \to 0}\frac{f(x + \Delta x) - f(x)}{\Delta x}$$

As an illustration of finding the slope of a curve at a given point, consider the point $P(3,-1)$ on the parabola $y = x^2 - 4x + 2$, as in Fig. 8-5.

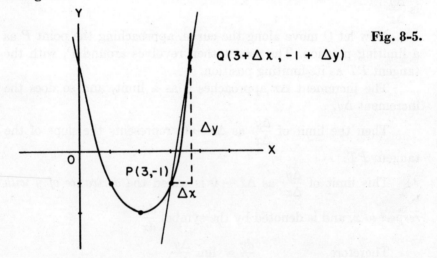

Fig. 8-5.

$Q(3+\Delta x, -1 + \Delta y)$

Assign to Δx a series of decreasing positive values and compute the corresponding values of Δy and $\dfrac{\Delta y}{\Delta x}$, as in the following table:

Δx	$3 + \Delta x$	$-1 + \Delta y$	Δy	$\Delta y/\Delta x$
1	4	-2.00	3	3
0.1	3.1	-0.79	0.21	2.1
0.01	3.01	-0.9799	0.0201	2.01
0.001	3.001	-0.997999	0.002001	2.001
0.0001	3.0001	-0.99979999	0.00020001	2.0001

The formation of one line of this table is illustrated by the following:

If $\Delta x = 0.1$,

then $x + \Delta x = 3 + 0.1 = 3.1$.

And $y + \Delta y = (3.1)^2 - 4(3.1) + 2$

$= 9.61 - 12.4 + 2$

$= -0.79$.

But at the point P, $y = -1$,

so $-1 + \Delta y = -0.79$

and $\Delta y = 0.21$.

Therefore, $\dfrac{\Delta y}{\Delta x} = \dfrac{0.21}{0.1} = 2.1$.

From an examination of the table, it *appears* that, as Δx approaches 0, $\dfrac{\Delta y}{\Delta x}$ approaches 2.

That 2 is *actually* the limit of $\dfrac{\Delta y}{\Delta x}$, as Δx approaches 0, is proved below.

Since the point $Q(3 + \Delta x, -1 + \Delta y)$ lies on the parabola $y = x^2 - 4x + 2$, its coordinates satisfy the equation of the parabola (Fig. 8-5).

Therefore, $-1 + \Delta y = (3 + \Delta x)^2 - 4(3 + \Delta x) + 2$

or $-1 + \Delta y = 9 + 6\overline{\Delta x} + \overline{\Delta x}^2 - 12 - 4\overline{\Delta x} + 2$.

Then $\Delta y = 2\overline{\Delta x} + \overline{\Delta x}^2$.

Divide by Δx: $\dfrac{\Delta y}{\Delta x} = 2 + \Delta x$.

Now take the limit of both sides, as $\Delta x \to 0$:

$$\lim_{\Delta x \to 0} \frac{\Delta y}{\Delta x} = \lim_{\Delta x \to 0} 2 + \lim_{\Delta x \to 0} \Delta x.$$

Then $\lim\limits_{\Delta x \to 0} \dfrac{\Delta y}{\Delta x} = 2 + 0$

or $$\frac{dy}{dx} = 2.$$

Therefore, the slope of the curve at $P(3,-1)$ is 2.

8-6 *Differentiation by the Delta Method*

The process of finding the derivative of a function, $f(x)$, at any given point is called *differentiation*, and to *differentiate* means to find the derivative.

The following example illustrates the general procedure.

EXAMPLE. Differentiate the function $y = -x^2 + 6x - 7$.

Let $P(x,y)$ be any point on the parabola
$$y = -x^2 + 6x - 7. \qquad [1]$$

Also, let $Q(x + \Delta x, y + \Delta y)$ be a neighboring point on the curve, as in Fig. 8-6.

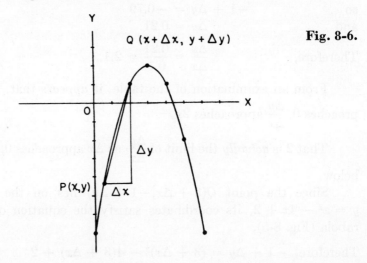

Fig. 8-6.

Since point Q lies on the curve, its coordinates must satisfy the equation of the curve [1].

Then $y + \Delta y = -(x + \Delta x)^2 + 6(x + \Delta x) - 7,$

and $\quad y + \Delta y = -x^2 - 2x\,\overline{\Delta x} - \overline{\Delta x}^2 + 6x + 6\overline{\Delta x} - 7. \qquad [2]$

Subtract equation [1] from equation [2]:
$$\Delta y = -2x\,\overline{\Delta x} - \overline{\Delta x}^2 + 6\overline{\Delta x}.$$

Divide by Δx: $\quad \dfrac{\Delta y}{\Delta x} = -2x - \overline{\Delta x} + 6.$

Take the limits of both sides as $\Delta x \to 0$.

Then $\qquad \lim\limits_{\Delta x \to 0} \dfrac{\Delta y}{\Delta x} = \lim\limits_{\Delta x \to 0} (-2x) - \lim\limits_{\Delta x \to 0} \Delta x + \lim\limits_{\Delta x \to 0} 6.$

Therefore, $\lim\limits_{\Delta x \to 0} \dfrac{\Delta y}{\Delta x} = -2x - 0 + 6$

or $\qquad\qquad \dfrac{dy}{dx} = -2x + 6.$ $\qquad\qquad\qquad$ [3]

To find the slope of the curve at any point, substitute the value of x at the given point in equation [3].

Thus, at the point (2,1),

$$\text{the slope} = -2(2) + 6 = -4 + 6 = 2.$$

At the point (3,2),

$$\text{the slope} = -2(3) + 6 = -6 + 6 = 0.$$

Although simpler methods for finding the derivatives of algebraic functions are derived in the next chapter, it must be remembered that this "delta" method is fundamental and is used for finding the derivatives of trigonometric, exponential, and logarithmic functions.

E X E R C I S E S

Differentiate the following functions:

1. $y = 3x^2.$
2. $y = 5x^2 - 2x.$
3. $y = x^2 - 3x + 5.$
4. $y = 2x^2 + 5x - 9.$
5. $y = x^3 - 5x - 7.$

Find by differentiation the slopes of the following curves at the points indicated:

6. $y = x^2 - 4x - 4; x = -1, 0.$
7. $y = -2x^2 + 6x - 3; x = 2, -2.$
8. $y = x^3 - 6x - 2; x = 1, -3.$
9. $y = 2x^3 - 3x - 4; x = \frac{1}{3}, -1.$
10. $y = x^3 + 2x^2 - 7; x = 1, -3.$
11. $y = 2x^3 - 4x^2 - 5; x = 2, \frac{1}{2}.$

12. $y = \frac{1}{2}x^2 - 3x - 2; x = 0, -\frac{1}{2}.$

13. $y = \frac{1}{x}; x = 1, -2.$

14. $y = \frac{2}{x + 1}; x = -2, -\frac{1}{2}.$

15. $y = \frac{x + 4}{x}; x = -2, 2, \frac{1}{2}.$

9

DIFFERENTIATION OF ALGEBRAIC FUNCTIONS

9-1 Introduction

In Chapter 8 the derivative of a function was found by the fundamental method, i.e., the "increment" or "delta" method. In this chapter, special rules are derived for finding the derivative of algebraic functions.

9-2 Derivative of ax^n

(a) n is a positive integer.

Let

$$y = ax^n. \tag{1}$$

Then

$$y + \Delta y = a(x + \Delta x)^n.$$

By the binomial expansion,

$$y + \Delta y = a\left[x^n + nx^{n-1}\overline{\Delta x} + \frac{n(n-1)}{2!}x^{n-2}\overline{\Delta x}^2 \right.$$
$$\left. + \frac{n(n-1)(n-2)}{3!}x^{n-3}\overline{\Delta x}^3 + \cdots + \overline{\Delta x}^n \right]. \tag{2}$$

103

Subtract [1] from [2]:

$$\Delta y = \left[nax^{n-1}\,\overline{\Delta x} + \frac{n(n-1)}{2!}\,ax^{n-2}\,\overline{\Delta x}^{2} \right.$$
$$\left. + \frac{n(n-1)(n-2)}{3!}\,ax^{n-3}\,\overline{\Delta x}^{3} + \cdots + a\,\overline{\Delta x}^{n} \right].$$

Divide both sides by Δx:

$$\frac{\Delta y}{\Delta x} = \left[nax^{n-1} + \frac{n(n-1)}{2!}\,ax^{n-2}\,\overline{\Delta x} \right.$$
$$\left. + \frac{n(n-1)(n-2)}{3!}\,ax^{n-3}\,\overline{\Delta x}^{2} + \cdots + a\,\overline{\Delta x}^{n-1} \right].$$

Take the limit of both sides as $\Delta x \to 0$:

$$\lim_{\Delta x \to 0}\frac{\Delta y}{\Delta x} = \lim_{\Delta x \to 0}\left[nax^{n-1} + \frac{n(n-1)}{2!}\,ax^{n-2}\,\overline{\Delta x} \right.$$
$$\left. + \frac{n(n-1)(n-2)}{3!}\,ax^{n-3}\,\overline{\Delta x}^{2} + \cdots + a\,\overline{\Delta x}^{n-1} \right].$$

Since the limit of the sum is the sum of the limits and since every term on the right after the first approaches 0 as a limit,

$$\lim_{\Delta x \to 0}\frac{\Delta y}{\Delta x} = nax^{n-1}.$$

Therefore,

$$\frac{dy}{dx} = nax^{n-1}. \qquad [3]$$

(b) n is not a positive integer.

Formula [3] is true for n not a positive integer, but the proof of this is beyond the scope of this text.

9-3 Other Notations for the Derivative

In addition to the symbol $\dfrac{dy}{dx}$, other notations are used to denote the derivative of $y = f(x)$ with respect to x. Those most commonly used are y', $f'(x)$ and $D_x y$.

For example, if

$$y = f(x) = ax^n,$$

then

$$\frac{dy}{dx} = y' = f'(x) = D_x y = nax^{n-1}.$$

EXAMPLE 1. Differentiate $y = 3x^5$.

$$\frac{dy}{dx} = (5)(3)x^{5-1}$$

$$= 15x^4.$$

EXAMPLE 2. Differentiate $y = \dfrac{2}{x}$.

Since
$$y = 2x^{-1},$$
$$D_x y = (-1)(2)x^{-1-1}$$
$$= -2x^{-2}$$
$$= -\frac{2}{x^2}.$$

EXAMPLE 3. Differentiate $y = \sqrt{x}$.

Since
$$y = x^{\frac{1}{2}}$$
$$\frac{dy}{dx} = \frac{1}{2}x^{\frac{1}{2}-1} = \frac{1}{2}x^{-\frac{1}{2}}$$
$$= \frac{1}{2\sqrt{x}}.$$

E X E R C I S E S

Differentiate the following functions:

1. $y = 5x^2$.

2. $y = 3x^5$.

3. $y = -x$.

4. $y = 2\sqrt{x^3}$.

5. $y = \dfrac{3}{\sqrt{x}}$.

6. $y = 4\sqrt[3]{x^2}$.

7. $y = -2x^{\frac{1}{2}}$.

8. $f(s) = 4s^2$.

9. $f(t) = -16t^2$.

10. $f(x) = \frac{1}{2}x^{-\frac{2}{3}}$.

11. $f(t) = -3t^{\frac{4}{3}}$.

12. $f(x) = -\dfrac{5}{\sqrt[5]{x^3}}$.

9-4 *Derivative of a Constant*

The locus of $y = c$ (where c is a constant) is a straight line parallel to the x-axis, and its slope at all points is zero. Hence, if $y = c$, $\dfrac{dy}{dx} = 0$. In other words, the derivative of a constant with respect to any variable is zero.

9-5 Derivative of a Sum of Functions

Let $u = f_1(x)$, $v = f_2(x)$ and $w = f_3(x)$ and let

$$y = u + v + w. \tag{1}$$

Then

$$y + \Delta y = (u + \Delta u) + (v + \Delta v) + (w + \Delta w). \tag{2}$$

Subtract [1] from [2]:

$$\Delta y = \Delta u + \Delta v + \Delta w.$$

Divide both sides by Δx:

$$\frac{\Delta y}{\Delta x} = \frac{\Delta w}{\Delta x} + \frac{\Delta v}{\Delta x} + \frac{\Delta w}{\Delta x}$$

Take the limit of both sides as $\Delta x \to 0$.

Therefore, $\quad \dfrac{dy}{dx} = \dfrac{du}{dx} + \dfrac{dv}{dx} + \dfrac{dw}{dx}. \tag{3}$

EXAMPLE. Find the derivative with respect to x of the function $y = 4x^3 - 3x^2 + 6x - 3 - 2x^{-1}$.

$$\frac{dy}{dx} = 12x^2 - 6x + 6 + 2x^{-2}.$$

E X E R C I S E S

Differentiate each of the following functions:

1. $y = 3x^2 - 4x - 2$.

2. $f(x) = ax^2 + bx + c$.

3. $y = 4x + 3$.

4. $y = 4x^4 + 5x^3 - 6x^2 + 7x - 3$.

5. $y = 5x^3 - 7x + 9 - 3x^{-2}$.

6. $y = 3x^{\frac{2}{3}} - 6x^{-\frac{1}{2}}$.

7. $y = 4x^{\frac{1}{2}} - 2 - 3x^{-\frac{1}{2}}$.

8. $f(x) = \dfrac{3}{x} + \dfrac{2}{x^2} - \dfrac{6}{\sqrt{x}}$.

9. $y = ax^3 - 3bx^2 + 6cx - \frac{7}{9}k$.

10. $f(x) = 5x^2 - 7x^{-1} + 3x^{-2}$.

11. $y = 2x^{\frac{2}{3}} - 4x^{\frac{1}{4}} - 2x^{-\frac{1}{2}}$.

12. $s = \dfrac{a + bt + ct^2}{\sqrt{t}}$.

Find the slopes of the following curves at the points whose values of x are given:

13. $y = 4x + 3; x = 0, -2.$

14. $y = x^2 - 4x + 2; x = 1, 0.$

15. $y = x^3 - 6x^2 - 4x + 2; x = -1, 8.$

16. $y = 2\sqrt{x} - 3\sqrt[3]{x}; x = 1, 8.$

For what values of x are the slopes of the following curves zero?

17. $y = 2x^3 + 3x^2 - 12x + 1.$

18. $y = x^3 + 3x^2.$

19. $y = 3x^2 - 12x + 12.$

20. $y = 4x^3 + 15x^2 - 72x + 6.$

9-6 Derivative of au^n, Where $u = f(x)$

For example, suppose $y = 3(2 - 3x)^4$. Here, $a = 3, u = 2 - 3x$ and $n = 4$.

The derivative of y with respect to x can be found by expanding $(2 - 3x)^4$ by the binomial theorem, multiplying each term by 3 and then finding the derivative of the resulting polynomial as in the previous section.

However, suppose $y = \sqrt{4 + x^2} = (4 + x^2)^{\frac{1}{2}}$. Here, $a = 1$, $u = 4 + x^2$ and $n = \frac{1}{2}$.

Although $(4 + x^2)^{\frac{1}{2}}$ can be expanded by the binomial theorem, the expansion is an infinite series, whose differentiation is beyond the scope of this text.

Accordingly, to carry out this differentiation where $y = u^n$ and $u = f(x)$, a new theorem is now derived.

Theorem: If $y = au^n$, where $u = f(x)$, then

$$\frac{dy}{dx} = nau^{n-1} \cdot \frac{du}{dx}.$$

Proof:

$$y = au^n, \tag{1}$$
$$y + \Delta y = a(u + \Delta u)^n.$$

By the binomial theorem,

$$y + \Delta y = a \left(u^n + n u^{n-1} \overline{\Delta u} + \frac{n(n-1)}{2!} u^{n-2} \overline{\Delta u}^2 \right.$$

$$\left. + \cdots + \overline{\Delta u}^n \right). \qquad [2]$$

Subtract [1] from [2]:

$$\Delta y = n a u^{n-1} \Delta u + \frac{n(n-1)}{2!} a u^{n-2} \overline{\Delta u}^2 + \cdots + a \overline{\Delta u}^n.$$

Divide both sides by Δx and note that

$$\frac{\overline{\Delta u}^2}{\Delta x} = \frac{\Delta u}{\Delta x} \cdot \Delta u, \quad \frac{\overline{\Delta u}^3}{\Delta x} = \frac{\Delta u}{\Delta x} \cdot \overline{\Delta u}^2, \text{ etc.}$$

Then

$$\frac{\Delta y}{\Delta x} = n a u^{n-1} \cdot \frac{\Delta u}{\Delta x} + \frac{n(n-1)}{2!} a u^{n-2} \cdot \frac{\Delta u}{\Delta x} \cdot \overline{\Delta u}$$

$$+ \cdots + a \frac{\Delta u}{\Delta x} \cdot \overline{\Delta u}^{n-1}.$$

Take the limits of both sides as $\Delta x \to 0$ and note that the limit of all the terms on the right side after the first is zero, since each of these terms contains a factor which is a power of Δu and $\Delta u \to 0$ as $\Delta x \to 0$.

Therefore, $\qquad \dfrac{dy}{dx} = n a u^{n-1} \cdot \dfrac{du}{dx}.$

This theorem is true for n when it is not a positive integer, but the proof is beyond the scope of this text.

EXAMPLE 1. Differentiate $y = 3(2 - 3x)^4$.

$$\frac{dy}{dx} = (4)(3)(2 - 3x)^3 (-3)$$

$$= -36(2 - 3x)^3.$$

EXAMPLE 2. Differentiate $y = \sqrt{4 + x^2}$

Since $\qquad y = (4 + x^2)^{\frac{1}{2}},$

$$\frac{dy}{dx} = \frac{1}{2}(4 + x^2)^{-\frac{1}{2}}(2x)$$

$$= x(4 + x^2)^{-\frac{1}{2}}$$

$$= \frac{x}{\sqrt{4 + x^2}}.$$

EXAMPLE 3. Differentiate $y = \dfrac{4}{2x - 1}$.

Since
$$y = 4(2x - 1)^{-1},$$

$$\frac{dy}{dx} = (-1)(4)(2x - 1)^{-2}(2)$$

$$= -\frac{8}{(2x - 1)^2}.$$

E X E R C I S E S

Differentiate the following functions:

1. $y = 2(2 - 3x)^3$.

2. $y = \sqrt{1 - x}$.

3. $f(x) = 2\sqrt{x^2 + 1}$.

4. $s = (t^2 - 3t - 1)^3$.

5. $y = 2(x^2 - 3)^{-5}$.

6. $f(r) = \sqrt{25 - r^2}$.

7. $y = (a + bx)^2$.

8. $y = 5(a^2 - x^2)^3$.

Find the slopes of the following curves at the points indicated:

9. $y = \sqrt{1 - 2x}$; $x = -2$.

10. $y = 2(3x^2 - 2)^2$; $x = 1, -1$.

11. $y = \dfrac{4}{2 - x}$; $x = -1, 3$.

12. $y = \dfrac{2}{1 + x^2}$; $x = -2, 3$.

13. $v = \dfrac{\pi r^2}{a^2}(a - x)^2$; $x = a, -a$.

14. In example 13, find the point on the curve at which the slope is zero.

9-7 Derivative of a Product of Two Functions

For example, suppose that $y = 3x(2 - 3x)^4$. This expression is of the form $y = uv$, where $u = f_1(x)$ and $v = f_2(x)$.

To find the derivative of this expression, the following theorem is derived.

Theorem: If $y = uv$, where $u = f_1(x)$ and $v = f_2(x)$ then

$$\frac{dy}{dx} = u \cdot \frac{dv}{dx} + v \cdot \frac{du}{dx}.$$

Proof:
$$y = uv. \tag{1}$$
$$y + \Delta y = (u + \Delta u)(v + \Delta v)$$
$$= uv + u \cdot \overline{\Delta v} + v \cdot \overline{\Delta u} + \overline{\Delta u} \cdot \overline{\Delta v}. \tag{2}$$

Subtract [1] from [2]:

$$\Delta y = u \cdot \overline{\Delta v} + v \cdot \overline{\Delta u} + \overline{\Delta u} \cdot \overline{\Delta v}.$$

Divide both sides by Δx:

$$\frac{\Delta y}{\Delta x} = u \cdot \frac{\Delta v}{\Delta x} + v \cdot \frac{\Delta u}{\Delta x} + \frac{\Delta u}{\Delta x} \cdot \Delta v.$$

Take the limit of both sides as $\Delta x \to 0$ and note that the third term of the right side approaches zero as a limit, because it contains as a factor Δv, which approaches zero as $\Delta x \to 0$.

Therefore,
$$\frac{dy}{dv} = u \cdot \frac{dv}{dx} + v \frac{du}{dx}.$$

As an aid to remembering this theorem, it may be stated in words as follows:

"The derivative of a product is the first function times the derivative of the second plus the second function times the derivative of the first."

EXAMPLE 1. Differentiate $y = 3x(2 - 3x)^4$.

Here, $u = 3x$ and $v = (2 - 3x)^4$.

Therefore, $\dfrac{du}{dx} = 3$ and $\dfrac{dv}{dx} = (4)(2 - 3x)^3(-3)$

$$= -12(2 - 3x)^3.$$

Then $\dfrac{dy}{dx} = 3x[-12(2 - 3x)^3] + (2 - 3x)^4(3)$

$$= -36x(2 - 3x)^3 + 3(2 - 3x)^4$$
$$= 3(2 - 3x)^3[-12x + (2 - 3x)]$$
$$= 3(2 - 3x)^3(2 - 15x).$$

EXAMPLE 2. Differentiate $y = x\sqrt{1 - 2x^2}$.

This can be written $y = x(1 - 2x^2)^{\frac{1}{2}}$,
where $u = x$ and $v = (1 - 2x^2)^{\frac{1}{2}}$.

Then $\dfrac{dy}{dx} = x\left(\dfrac{1}{2}\right)(1 - 2x^2)^{-\frac{1}{2}}(-4x) + (1 - 2x^2)^{\frac{1}{2}}(1)$

$$= -\frac{2x^2}{(1 - 2x^2)^{\frac{1}{2}}} + (1 - 2x^2)^{\frac{1}{2}}$$

$$= \frac{-2x^2 + (1 - 2x^2)}{(1 - 2x^2)^{\frac{1}{2}}}$$

$$= \frac{1 - 4x^2}{(1 - 2x^2)^{\frac{1}{2}}}$$

$$= \frac{1 - 4x^2}{\sqrt{1 - 2x^2}}.$$

E X E R C I S E S

Differentiate the following functions:

1. $y = 2x(2 - 3x)^2$.

2. $y = (x - 5)^3(2x - 3)^2$.

3. $y = (x^2 + 2)^2(x^2 - 2)^2$.

4. $f(x) = (x^2 + 5x - 3)(x^2 - x - 5)$.

5. $f(x) = x\sqrt{a + bx}$.

6. $f(t) = t^2\sqrt{1 - t}$.

7. $y = 2x^2\sqrt{x^2 - 1}$.

8. $y = \dfrac{b}{a}x\sqrt{a^2 - x^2}$.

9. $y = 3x\sqrt{1 - 2x^2}$.

10. $f(x) = x(8 - x^2)^5$.

11. $y = \sqrt{x^2 - 3}\,\sqrt{x^2 + 3}$.

12. $y = \sqrt{x}\,\sqrt[3]{x - 1}$.

13. $y = x^3(x^3 + 1)^3$.

14. $y = \sqrt{x}\,(1 + x^3)^2$. $(1+x^3)(1+13x)^3$

In each of the following functions, find the value of the derivative for the given value of x: $2(x)^{\frac{1}{2}}$

15. $y = x\sqrt{9 - x}$; $x = 0, 3$.

16. $y = 2x\sqrt{25 - x^2}$; $x = 4, -4$. $-\frac{14}{3} - \frac{14}{3}$

17. $y = x^2\sqrt{3 - 4x}$; $x = 0, \frac{1}{2}$. $\frac{44}{64} \quad 0$

18. $f(x) = 2x(9 - x^2)^2$; $x = 1, -1,3$.

9-8 Derivative of a Quotient of Two Functions

If the function

$$y = \frac{3x}{3 - 2x^2}$$

is written as the product of two functions

$$y = 3x(3 - 2x^2)^{-1},$$

it can be differentiated as in the preceding section.

However, considerable manipulation can be saved by deriving a special formula for the differentiation of a quotient, as follows:

Theorem: If $y = \dfrac{u}{v}$, where $u = f_1(x)$ and $v = f_2(x)$, then

$$\frac{dy}{dx} = \frac{v \cdot \dfrac{du}{dx} - u \cdot \dfrac{dv}{dx}}{v^2}.$$

Proof: $y = \dfrac{u}{v}$ may be written as $y = uv^{-1}$.

By the theorem for the differentiation of a product,

$$\frac{dy}{dx} = u \cdot \frac{d(v^{-1})}{dx} + v^{-1} \cdot \frac{du}{dx}.$$

This reduces to

$$\frac{dy}{dx} = u(-1)(v^{-2}) \cdot \frac{dv}{dx} + v^{-1} \cdot \frac{du}{dx}$$

$$= -\frac{u}{v^2} \cdot \frac{dv}{dx} + \frac{1}{v} \cdot \frac{du}{dx}$$

$$\frac{dy}{dx} = \frac{v \cdot \dfrac{du}{dx} - u \cdot \dfrac{dv}{dx}}{v^2}.$$

As an aid to remembering this theorem, it may be stated in words as follows:

"The derivative of a quotient is the denominator times the derivative of the numerator minus the numerator times the derivative of the denominator, all divided by the denominator squared."

EXAMPLE 1. Differentiate $y = \dfrac{3x}{3 - 2x^2}$.

$$\frac{dy}{dx} = \frac{(3 - 2x^2)(3) - (3x)(-4x)}{(3 - 2x^2)^2}$$

$$= \frac{9 - 6x^2 + 12x^2}{(3 - 2x^2)^2}$$

$$= \frac{9 + 6x^2}{(3 - 2x^2)^2}$$

$$= \frac{3(3 + 2x^2)}{(3 - 2x^2)^2}.$$

EXAMPLE 2. Differentiate $y = \dfrac{x}{\sqrt{3x^2 - 2}}.$

This may be written

$$y = \frac{x}{(3x^2 - 2)^{\frac{1}{2}}}.$$

Then $\quad \dfrac{dy}{dx} = \dfrac{(3x^2 - 2)^{\frac{1}{2}}(1) - x(\frac{1}{2})(3x^2 - 2)^{-\frac{1}{2}}(6x)}{(3x^2 - 2)}.$

Multiply numerator and denominator by $(3x^2 - 2)^{\frac{1}{2}}$:

$$\frac{dy}{dx} = \frac{(3x^2 - 2) - (3x^2)(1)}{(3x^2 - 2)^{\frac{3}{2}}}$$

$$= -\frac{2}{(3x^2 - 2)^{\frac{3}{2}}}.$$

E X E R C I S E S

Differentiate the following functions:

1. $y = \dfrac{x}{1 - x}.$

2. $f(x) = \dfrac{2 + 3x}{3 - 2x}.$

3. $y = \dfrac{1 - x^2}{2 - x}.$

4. $y = \dfrac{\sqrt{1 + x}}{2x}.$

5. $y = \dfrac{2x}{2 + x}.$

6. $y = \dfrac{\sqrt{9 - x^2}}{2x}.$

7. $y = \dfrac{x^2 + 1}{x - 1}.$

8. $s = \dfrac{a + t}{(a - t)^2}.$

9. $f(x) = \dfrac{3x}{1 - 3x}.$

10. $f(r) = \dfrac{1 - r}{\sqrt{1 + r}}.$

11. $f(x) = \dfrac{a^2 + x^2}{\sqrt{2ax}}.$

12. Find the slope of $y = \dfrac{x^2 + 2}{x - 2}$ at the points where the values of x are 0, $-\frac{1}{2}$, 3, and 4.

Differentiate the following functions:

1. $y = 3(2 - 3x)^3$.

2. $y = 3x(2 - 3x)^3$.

3. $y = 2\sqrt{1 + x^2}$.

4. $y = 2x\sqrt{1 + x^2}$.

5. $y = \dfrac{x^3 - 1}{x}$.

6. $y = \dfrac{x}{x^3 - 1}$.

7. $f(x) = 2\sqrt{x} - 3\sqrt[3]{x}$.

8. $s = \dfrac{1}{t} + \dfrac{1}{t^2} + \dfrac{1}{t^3}$.

9. $y = \dfrac{a}{b}\sqrt{a^2 - x^2}$.

10. $y = \dfrac{x}{a}\sqrt{a^2 - x^2}$.

11. $x^2y - y - 2 = 0$ [*Hint:* Solve for y].

12. Find the slope of $y = \dfrac{x}{x - 1}$ at the points where the values of x are $-1, 0, 2$, and 3.

10

APPLICATIONS OF THE DERIVATIVE

10-1 *Increasing and Decreasing Functions*

An *increasing function* is a function whose value is increasing as the value of the independent variable increases.

A *decreasing function* is a function whose value is decreasing as the value of the independent variable increases.

The *differential calculus* furnishes a simple method of determining when a function is increasing and when it is decreasing.

It was shown in Section 8-5 that, if $y = f(x)$ is the equation of a curve, as in Fig. 10-1, then $\dfrac{dy}{dx}$ equals the slope of the tangent to the curve at any given point.

An examination of Fig. 10-1, shows that

(a) When the curve is rising, i.e., when the function is increasing, the tangent to the curve makes an acute angle with the x-axis. Hence, the slope is positive, as at point P_1.

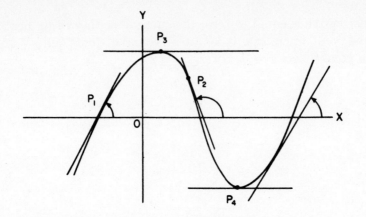

Fig. 10-1.

(b) When the curve is falling, i.e., when the function is decreasing, the tangent to the curve makes an obtuse angle with the x-axis. Hence, the slope is negative, as at point P_2.

(c) When the curve is neither rising nor falling, i.e., when the function is neither increasing nor decreasing, the tangent to the curve is parallel to the x-axis. Hence, the slope is zero, as at points P_3 and P_4. Therefore, the derivative $\dfrac{dy}{dx}$ is

(a) *positive* at points where the curve is *rising;*
(b) *negative* at points where the curve is *falling;*
(c) *zero* at points where the curve is *neither rising nor falling.*

Points on the curve where the derivative is equal to zero are called *critical points.*

EXAMPLE. Determine whether the curve $y = x^3 - 3x^2 + 3$ is rising, falling, or critical at the points where $x = -1, 0, 1, 2$.

If
$$y = x^3 - 3x^2 + 3,$$
then
$$\frac{dy}{dx} = 3x^2 - 6x = 3x(x - 2).$$

At the point where $x = -1$,
$$\frac{dy}{dx} = (-3)(-3) = 9.$$

Since the derivative is positive, the curve is rising at the point where $x = -1$.

At the point where $x = 0$,
$$\frac{dy}{dx} = (0)(-2) = 0.$$

Since the derivative is equal to zero, the curve is neither rising nor falling at the point where $x = 0$, i.e., it is critical at this point.

At the point where $x = 1$,

$$\frac{dy}{dx} = (3)(-1) = -3.$$

Since the derivative is negative, the curve is falling at the point where $x = 1$.

At the point where $x = 2$,

$$\frac{dy}{dx} = (6)(0) = 0.$$

Since the derivative is zero, the curve is neither rising nor falling at the point where $x = 2$, i.e., it is critical at this point.

These conclusions can be checked by reference to the graph of the function, as shown in Fig. 10-2.

$y = x^3 - 3x^2 + 3$

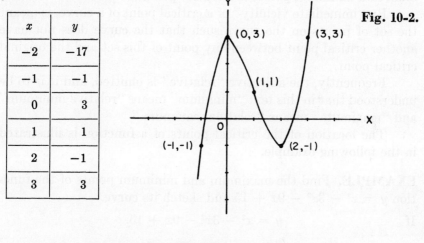

Fig. 10-2.

x	y
-2	-17
-1	-1
0	3
1	1
2	-1
3	3

E X E R C I S E S

Determine whether the following curves are rising, falling, or critical at the points where x has the indicated values:

1. $y = x^2 + 6x + 9$; $x = -5, -3, 1$.

2. $y = 5 + 4x - 2x^2$; $x = -2, 1, 3$.

3. $y = x^3 - 3x - 3$; $x = -2, 1, 2$.

4. $y = x^3 - x^2 + 5$; $x = -2, 0, 2$.

5. $y = x^3 - 12x - 5$; $x = -1, 2, 4$.

6. $y = x^4 - 4x^2 + 2x - 2$; $x = -1, 2, 0$.

7. $y = -2x^3 - 3x^2 + 12x + 10$; $x = -1, 0, 1$.

8. $y = x^3 - 6x^2 + 9x - 2$; $x = \frac{1}{3}, 1, 2$.

9. $y = \dfrac{5x}{x^2 + 1}$; $x = 2, \frac{1}{2}$.

10. $y = x\sqrt{9 + x^2}$; $x = -1, 2, 0$.

10-2 *Maximum and Minimum Values of Functions*

A function $f(x)$ is said to have a *relative maximum value*, when, for a given value of $x = x_1$, the function is greater in value than for any other value of x in the immediate vicinity of x_1.

Also, a function $f(x)$ has a *relative minimum* value, when, for a given value of $x = x_2$, the function is less in value than for any other value of x in the immediate vicinity of x_2.

From Fig. 10-1 (page 116), it can be seen that relative maximum and minimum points are critical points of the curve.

By "immediate vicinity" of a critical point of a curve, is meant the set of points on the curve such that the curve does not have another critical point between any point of this set and the original critical point.

Frequently, the adjective "relative" is omitted, and it is to be understood that in this text "minimum" means "relative minimum" and "maximum" means "relative maximum."

The location of the critical points of a function is illustrated in the following example.

EXAMPLE. Find the maximum and minimum points of the function $y = x^3 - 3x^2 - 9x + 15$ and sketch its curve.

If
$$y = x^3 - 3x^2 - 9x + 15,$$

then
$$\frac{dy}{dx} = 3x^2 - 6x - 9.$$

Equate the derivative to zero, to locate the critical points:
$$3(x^2 - 2x - 3) = 0$$
$$3(x - 3)(x + 1) = 0.$$

Therefore, $x = 3$ and $x = -1$ are the critical values of x.

From the given equation, if $x = -1$, $y = 20$ and if $x = 3$, $y = -12$. Thus, it is seen that $(-1, 20)$ is a maximum point on the curve and $(3, -12)$ is a minimum point on the curve. These values make it possible to determine a reasonable scale for y in the sketch of the curve, as shown in Fig. 10-3.

$y = x^3 - 3x^2 - 9x + 15$

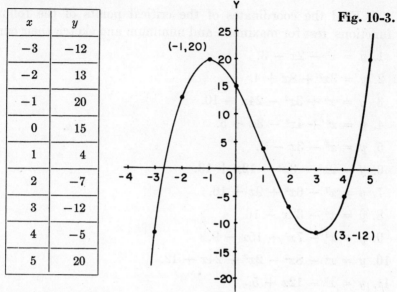

x	y
-3	-12
-2	13
-1	20
0	15
1	4
2	-7
3	-12
4	-5
5	20

Fig. 10-3.

While the sketch of the curve in Fig. 10-3 clearly indicates that $(-1,20)$ is a maximum point on the curve and $(3,-12)$ is a minimum point on the curve, the following analytic test for maximum and minimum is usually carried out.

First, substitute in the derivative, $3(x - 3)(x + 1)$, a value of x a little less than the critical value of $x = -1$, then a value of x a little more than the value of -1, and consider only the signs of the factors.

Thus, if $x < -1$, then $(-)(-) = +$ and the derivative is *positive*.

If $x > -1$, then $(-)(+) = -$ and the derivative is *negative*.

Since the derivative changes sign from plus through zero to minus at the point $(-1,20)$, this point is a maximum.

Next, test the point $(3,-12)$ in the same manner, using a value of x a little less than the critical value of $x = 3$ and a value of x a little more than the value of 3.

Thus, if $x < 3$, then $(-)(+) = -$ and the derivative is negative.

If $x > 3$, then $(+)(+) = +$ and the derivative is positive.

Since the derivative changes sign from minus through zero to plus at the point $(3,-12)$, this point is a minimum.

Applications of the Derivative / 119

E X E R C I S E S

Find the coordinates of the critical points of the following functions, test for maximum and minimum and sketch their curves:

1. $y = x^2 - 2x - 3$.

2. $y = 3x^2 + 8x + 4$.

3. $y = x^3 + 3x^2 - 24x - 10$.

4. $y = x^3 + 4x^2 - 3x + 5$.

5. $y = x^3 - 3x - 2$.

6. $y = 2x^3 - 3x^2 - 12x + 13$.

7. $y = x^3 - 6x^2 + 9x + 16$.

8. $y = x^4 - 32x - 16$.

9. $y = x^3 - 7x^2 + 15x - 9$.

10. $y = x^4 - 8x^3 - 2x^2 + 24x + 12$.

11. $y = x^3 - 12x + 5$.

12. $y = x^3 - 3x^2 - 9x + 24$.

13. $y = 2x^3 - 3x^2 - 12x + 13$.

14. $y = \frac{1}{3}x^3 - x^2 - 3x + 1$.

10-3 *Applied Problems—Maxima and Minima*

The application of differentiation to maxima and minima problems is best illustrated by the consideration of several specific examples.

EXAMPLE 1. A rectangular piece of metal 12 inches by 18 inches is to be made into an open box by cutting out equal squares from the corners and folding up the flaps (with no allowance for seams). What should be the size of the cut-out squares in order that the volume of the box shall be a maximum? What is the volume of this box?

First, an approximate solution obtained without the aid of the calculus is given, in order that the use of the differential calculus will be better understood and appreciated.

Accordingly, denote the volume of the box by V and the side of the cutout square by s, as in Fig. 10-4.

From the figure, it is seen that

$$V = s(18 - 2s)(12 - 2s),$$

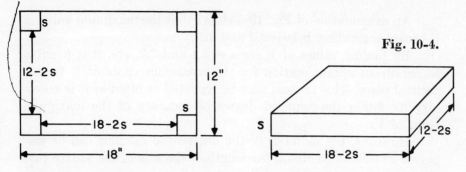

Fig. 10-4.

where the domain is $0 < s < 6$, since the shorter side of the metal is 12, which requires that the side of the cutout square be less than 6, or there would be no box.

A table of values of V and s can be made for values of s from 0 to 6.

If $\quad\quad s = 1, \quad V = (1)(16)(10) = 160,$

and if $\quad\quad s = 2, \quad V = (2)(14)(8) \ = 224, \quad$ etc.

Therefore,

s	0	$\frac{1}{2}$	1	$1\frac{1}{2}$	2	$2\frac{1}{2}$	3	$3\frac{1}{2}$	4	$4\frac{1}{2}$	5	$5\frac{1}{2}$	6
V	0	94	160	202	224	227	216	192	160	121	80	38	0

These corresponding values of V and s may be graphed, as in Fig. 10-5.

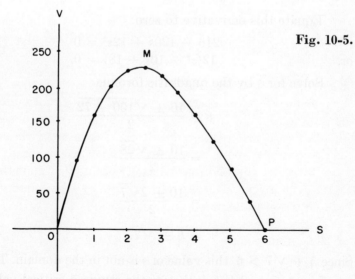

Fig. 10-5.

An examination of Fig. 10-5 shows that the maximum value of V occurs somewhere between 2 and 3.

By finding values of V for $s = 2.1$ and 2.2, etc. it is possible to obtain an approximation for the maximum value of V to one decimal place. This process may be repeated as often as it is necessary to obtain the required degree of accuracy of the maximum value of V.

However, the methods of the differential calculus can be employed as follows to obtain the length of the side of the square that gives the maximum value of the volume.

By reference to Fig. 10-5, it is seen that the curve is rising from O to a certain point M, is critical at point M, and is falling from M to point P.

Hence, the derivative of the function is *positive* from O to M, *equal to zero* at point M, and *negative* from M to point P.

Therefore, to find the maximum value of V, it is only necessary to take the derivative of V with respect to s, i.e., $\dfrac{dV}{ds}$, equate this derivative to zero, and solve the resulting equation for s. These values of s locate the critical points of the curve.

Thus, if
$$V = s(18 - 2s)(12 - 2s)$$
$$= 216s - 60s^2 + 4s^3.$$

Then
$$\frac{dV}{ds} = 216 - 120s + 12s^2.$$

Equate this derivative to zero:
$$216 - 120s + 12s^2 = 0$$

or,
$$12(s^2 - 10s + 18) = 0.$$

Solve for s by the quadratic formula:
$$s = \frac{10 \pm \sqrt{100 - 72}}{2}$$
$$= \frac{10 \pm \sqrt{28}}{2}$$
$$= \frac{10 \pm 2\sqrt{7}}{2}$$
$$= 5 \pm \sqrt{7}.$$

Since $5 + \sqrt{7} > 6$, this value of s is not in the domain. This leaves $s = 5 - \sqrt{7} = 2.4 +$ inches as the required critical value of s.

To test for a maximum, substitute in the derivative a value for s that is a little less than the critical value 2.4—for example, $s = 2$ —and then a value for s a little greater than 2.4—for example, $s = 3$—and note the signs of the derivative.

Thus, if $s = 2$,

$$\frac{dV}{ds} = 12(4 - 20 + 18) = +24$$

and, if $s = 3$,

$$\frac{dV}{ds} = 12(9 - 30 + 18) = -36.$$

Since the derivative changes sign from plus through zero to minus at the point where $s = 2.4 +$, this value of s gives a maximum value for the volume V.

The corresponding (maximum) value of V is obtained by substituting $s = 2.4 +$ in the original equation:

$$V = 2.4(18 - 4.8)\,(12 - 4.8)$$
$$V = 2.4(13.2)\,(7.2)$$
$$V = 228 + \text{cubic inches.}$$

In solving maxima and minima problems, the following method of procedure is suggested:

(a) Draw a figure to illustrate the problem and mark on it the constants and the variables.

(b) Write an equation with the quantity whose maximum or minimum is to be found, in terms of *one* of the other variables.

(c) Find the derivative of the dependent variable in terms of the independent variable.

(d) Simplify the derivative, preferably in factored form.

(e) Solve the derivative-equation for the critical values of the independent variable.

(f) Although in most applied problems it is usually easy to see which critical value gives a maximum and which gives a minimum, in some cases it may be necessary to apply one of the tests for a maximum or a minimum.

EXAMPLE 2. A man who is in a boat 3 miles from A, the nearest point on a straight shore, wishes to reach in the shortest time a point, B, which is on the shore and at a distance of 6 miles from A. If the man can row at the rate of 3 miles per hour and walk at the rate of 5 miles per hour, find the point of the shore toward which he should row.

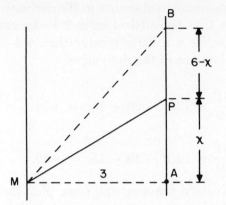

Fig. 10-6.

Let P (Fig. 10-6) be the point toward which the man rows.

While the distance MB is the shortest distance from M to B, it is not the fastest way of going, since the man can walk faster than he can row.

Since it is desired to find the minimum time to go from M to B, the time t is expressed as a function of the distance x (see Fig. 10-6).

The distance $MP = \sqrt{9 + x^2}$ and since the time equals the distance divided by the rate, the time to travel the distance MP is equal to $\dfrac{\sqrt{9 + x^2}}{3}$.

Also the time to travel the distance PB equals $\dfrac{6 - x}{5}$.

Therefore, $\qquad t = \dfrac{\sqrt{9 + x^2}}{3} + \dfrac{6 - x}{5}$,

or $\qquad\qquad t = \dfrac{1}{3}(9 + x^2)^{\frac{1}{2}} + \dfrac{6}{5} - \dfrac{1}{5}x$.

Differentiating,

$$\frac{dt}{dx} = \left(\frac{1}{2}\right)\left(\frac{1}{3}\right)(9 + x^2)^{-\frac{1}{2}}(2x) - \frac{1}{5},$$

or $\qquad\qquad \dfrac{dt}{dx} = \dfrac{x}{3(9 + x^2)^{\frac{1}{2}}} - \dfrac{1}{5}.$

Equate the derivative to zero:

$$\frac{x}{3(9 + x^2)^{\frac{1}{2}}} - \frac{1}{5} = 0.$$

Then $\qquad\qquad 5x - 3(9 + x^2)^{\frac{1}{2}} = 0$

and $\qquad\qquad\qquad 5x = 3(9 + x^2)^{\frac{1}{2}}.$

Square both sides:
$$25x^2 = 9(9 + x^2)$$
$$= 81 + 9x^2,$$
$$16x^2 = 81,$$
$$x^2 = \frac{81}{16},$$
$$x = \pm \frac{9}{4}.$$

Since the domain of the function is $0 \le x \le 6$, $x = -\frac{9}{4}$ is not in the domain. This leaves $x = \frac{9}{4}$ as the only value of x for which there is a critical value of t.

Therefore, the man should row toward a point P, which is $2\frac{1}{4}$ miles from the point A.

Although it is seen from the context of the problem that the time t has a minimum value when $x = 2\frac{1}{4}$, it is possible to test whether $x = 2\frac{1}{4}$ gives a maximum or minimum value for the time t, by employing the procedure which is suggested in the previous section of this chapter.

Thus, if a value is assigned to x which is a little less than the critical value of $2\frac{1}{4}$, for example 2, and this value is substituted for x in the derivative, then

$$\frac{dt}{dx} = \frac{2}{3\sqrt{13}} - \frac{1}{5}$$
$$= \frac{2\sqrt{13}}{39} - \frac{1}{5}$$
$$= 0.18 - 0.20$$
$$= -0.02.$$

Therefore, at the point where $x = 2$, the derivative is *negative*.

Next, assign to x a value a little greater than the critical value of $2\frac{1}{4}$, for example 3, and substitute for x in the derivative,

$$\frac{dt}{dx} = \frac{3}{3\sqrt{18}} - \frac{1}{5}$$
$$= \frac{\sqrt{2}}{6} - \frac{1}{5}$$
$$= 0.23 - 0.20$$
$$= 0.03.$$

Therefore, at the point where $x = 3$, the derivative is positive.

Since the derivative of the function changes in sign from minus through zero to plus, the function has a minimum at the point where $x = 2\frac{1}{4}$.

EXAMPLE 3. The stiffness of a rectangular beam varies as its breadth and the cube of its depth. Find the dimensions of the stiffest beam which can be cut from a circular log 12 inches in diameter.

Let S = the stiffness, b = the breadth, and h = the depth of the log, as shown in Fig. 10-7.

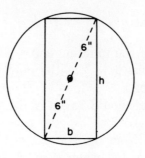

Fig. 10-7.

Therefore, $$S = kbh^3.$$

Since there are two variables on the right side of this equation, it is necessary to eliminate one of these variables and express S as a function of only one variable.

From the figure, $\qquad h = \sqrt{144 - b^2}$

and $\qquad\qquad\qquad h^3 = (144 - b^2)^{\frac{3}{2}}.$

By substitution, $\qquad S = kb(144 - b^2)^{\frac{3}{2}}.$

From Fig. 10-7, it is seen that the domain is $0 < b < 12$, since if b is 0 or 12 there can be no beam.

Differentiate:

$$\frac{dS}{db} = k[(b)(\tfrac{3}{2})(144 - b^2)^{\frac{1}{2}}(-2b) + (144 - b^2)^{\frac{3}{2}}(1)]$$
$$= k[-3b^2(144 - b^2)^{\frac{1}{2}} + (144 - b^2)^{\frac{3}{2}}]$$
$$= k(144 - b^2)^{\frac{1}{2}}(-3b^2 + 144 - b^2)$$
$$= k(144 - b^2)^{\frac{1}{2}}(144 - 4b^2).$$

Equate this derivative to zero:

$$k(144 - b^2)^{\frac{1}{2}}(144 - 4b^2) = 0.$$

Therefore,

$$
\begin{array}{ll}
k(144 - b^2)^{\frac{1}{2}} = 0, & 144 - 4b^2 = 0, \\
(144 - b^2)^{\frac{1}{2}} = 0, & 4b^2 = 144, \\
144 - b^2 = 0, & b^2 = 36, \\
b^2 = 144, & b = \pm6. \\
b = \pm12.
\end{array}
$$

Since $b = -6$, -12, and 12 are not in the domain, $b = 6$ is the only possible value for the breadth of the log.

Further, the corresponding value of h is $h = \sqrt{144 - 36}$ or $h = \sqrt{108} = 6\sqrt{3}$.

Therefore the dimensions of the beam are 6 inches by $6\sqrt{3}$ inches.

From the context of the problem, it is seen that S has a maximum value when $b = 6$. However, it is possible to test this value of b in the manner of the previous examples.

The actual testing of this value of b is left to the student as an exercise.

E X E R C I S E S

1. Find the dimensions of the stiffest rectangular beam that can be cut from a circular log 10 inches in diameter.

2. Find the dimensions of the largest rectangle that can be inscribed in a circle whose radius is r.

3. Find the dimensions and area of the largest rectangle that can be inclosed by a line 100 feet long.

4. Find the dimensions of the rectangle of the least perimeter whose area is 36 square feet.

5. Determine the constant k such that $y = x + \dfrac{k}{x}$ shall have a maximum at $x = 2$.

6. Find the dimensions and area of the largest rectangle whose perimeter is 30 feet.

7. Find two numbers whose sum is 32, such that the sum of their squares is a minimum.

8. A square piece of tin, 24 inches on a side, is to be made into an open box by cutting out equal squares from the corners and bending up the flaps. Find the side of the cutout square so that the volume of the box shall be a maximum.

9. Find the length of the base of an isosceles triangle of maximum area, if its two equal legs are 12 inches long.

10. Strips of tin 20 inches wide are to be made into a rectangular

open gutter by bending, as shown in the figure. x $\boxed{}$ x

$$20 - 2x$$

Determine the dimensions of the gutter for the maximum carrying capacity.

11. The strength of a rectangular beam varies as the width and the square of its depth. Find the dimensions of the strongest rectangular beam that can be cut from a circular log 12 inches in diameter.

12. If three sides of a trapezoid are each 6 inches long, how long must the fourth side be so that the area of the trapezoid shall be a maximum? $[A = \frac{1}{2}h(b + b^1)]$

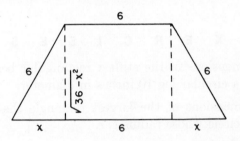

Fig. 10-8.

13. A rectangular box with a square base and an open top is to be constructed. Find the dimensions and the volume of the largest box that can be made from 675 square inches of material.

10-4 Applied Problems—Related Rates

If a body moves at a constant velocity, the distance which it travels is equal to the product of its velocity and time, i.e., $s = vt$, and the velocity is equal to the distance divided by the time, i.e.,

$$v = \frac{s}{t}.$$

However, if the velocity is not constant it is necessary to find the velocity at a specific instant of time, t. For this purpose, let the distance traversed be some function of the time, as for example, $s = f(t)$, whose graph is given in Fig. 10-9.

During the interval of time Δt the body moves the distance Δs. Then the *average velocity* during the time t is $\frac{\Delta s}{\Delta t}$, and

$$\lim_{\Delta t \to 0} \frac{\Delta s}{\Delta t} = \frac{ds}{dt}$$

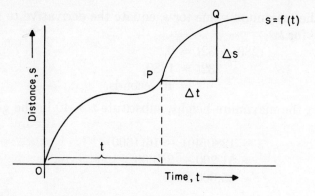

Fig. 10-9.

is the *instantaneous velocity* at the time t, and is the rate of change of s with respect to t.

In the case where y is a function of x and x is a function of t, i.e., $y = f(x)$ where $x = g(t)$, it is necessary to derive an additional formula in order to find the derivative of y with respect to t, $\dfrac{dy}{dt}$, as follows:

$$\frac{\Delta y}{\Delta t} = \frac{\Delta y}{\Delta x} \cdot \frac{\Delta x}{\Delta t}.$$

(This relationship holds true, since all the quantities are finite and the right side reduces to the left side.)

Take the limit of both sides as $\Delta t \to 0$:

$$\lim_{\Delta t \to 0} \frac{\Delta y}{\Delta t} = \lim_{\Delta x \to 0} \frac{\Delta y}{\Delta x} \cdot \lim_{\Delta x \to 0} \frac{\Delta x}{\Delta t}.$$

Therefore,
$$\frac{dy}{dt} = \frac{dy}{dx} \cdot \frac{dx}{dt}.$$

EXAMPLE 1. If a bullet is shot vertically upward, its height at any time is given by the formula $s = v_0 t - \frac{1}{2}gt^2$. If $v_0 = 1280$ feet per second and $g = 32$ feet per second per second, what was the velocity of the bullet after 12 seconds? How long did the bullet rise? How high did it rise?

If $\qquad s = 1280t - 16t^2,$

then $\qquad \dfrac{ds}{dt} = 1280 - 32t.$

(a) If $t = 12$,

$$\frac{ds}{dt} = 1280 - 384 = 896 \text{ feet per second.}$$

(b) To find the maximum value for s, equate the derivative to zero and solve for t:
$$1280 - 32t = 0,$$
$$32t = 1280,$$
$$t = 40 \text{ seconds.}$$

(c) To obtain the maximum height, substitute $t = 40$ in the given equation:
$$s = 1280(40) - 16(1600)$$
$$= 51,200 - 25,600$$
$$= 25,600 \text{ feet.}$$

EXAMPLE 2. The length of the side of a square is increasing at the rate of 0.3 inch per second. At what rate is the area of the square increasing, when the side is 10 inches long?

If x is the side of the square, then the area is $A = x^2$, and, since the rate of increase of the side x is 0.3 inch per second,

$$\frac{dx}{dt} = 0.3.$$

Now, $\quad \dfrac{dA}{dt} = 2x \cdot \dfrac{dx}{dt}.$

Therefore $\dfrac{dA}{dt} = 2(10)(0.3) = 6$ square inches per second.

EXAMPLE 3. A ladder 20 feet long leans against the vertical wall of a building. If the lower end of the ladder is drawn out along the horizontal ground at the rate of 2 feet per second, at what rate is the upper end of the ladder moving down the wall, when the lower end is 10 feet from the wall?

In Fig. 10-10, $x =$ the distance of the lower end of the ladder from the foot of the wall and $y =$ the distance of the upper end of the ladder from the foot of the wall.

Fig. 10-10.

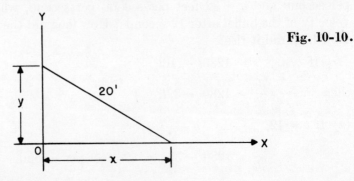

From the figure, $\qquad y = \sqrt{400 - x^2}$,
or $\qquad\qquad\qquad y = (400 - x^2)^{\frac{1}{2}}.$

Therefore,

$$\frac{dy}{dt} = \frac{1}{2}(400 - x^2)^{-\frac{1}{2}}(-2x) \cdot \frac{dx}{dt}$$

$$= -\frac{x}{\sqrt{400 - x^2}} \cdot \frac{dx}{dt}.$$

But, since the end of the ladder is moving out from the wall at the rate of 2 feet per second,

$$\frac{dx}{dt} = 2.$$

Therefore,

$$\frac{dy}{dt} = -\frac{2x}{\sqrt{400 - x^2}}.$$

When $x = 10$,

$$\frac{dy}{dt} = -\frac{20}{\sqrt{400 - 100}} = -\frac{20}{\sqrt{300}}$$

$$= -\frac{20}{10\sqrt{3}} = -\frac{2}{\sqrt{3}}$$

$$= -\frac{2}{3}\sqrt{3} \text{ feet per second.}$$

Therefore,

$$\frac{dy}{dt} = -1.15 \text{ feet per second (approximately).}$$

The negative sign shows that y is a decreasing function, and that the top of the ladder is moving *down* the wall.

E X E R C I S E S

1. If the distance s is measured in feet and t in seconds, find the velocity at the end of 5 seconds of bodies which move according to the following laws: $s = 35t + 16t^2$; $s = 2t^2 + 5t - 3$; $s = 5t^2 - 4t + 20$; $s = \frac{1}{3}t^3 + 15t^2 - 4t$.

2. A body is moving according to the law $s = 160t - 16t^2$. When will the body stop moving? How far will it go?

3. The radius of a spherical soap bubble is increasing at the rate of 0.1 inch per second. At what rate is the volume of the bubble increasing, when its radius is 2 inches? ($V = \frac{4}{3}\pi r^3$)

4. A 40-foot ladder is leaning against a wall. If the bottom of the ladder is moving away from the wall at the rate of 2 feet per minute, at what rate is the top of the ladder moving down the wall when the foot of the ladder is 24 feet from the wall?

5. The volume of a spherical soap bubble is increasing at the rate of 2 cubic inches per second. At what rate is the radius increasing, when the radius is 2 inches?

6. The volume of a given quantity of gas varies with the pressure according to the law $PV = 5000$. If the pressure is increasing at the rate of 0.3 unit per minute, how fast is the volume changing when $P = 10$?

7. A kite which is 125 feet high is drifting away horizontally at the rate of 5 feet per second. How fast is the string being played out when the length of the string is 225 feet? (Assume that the string is taut.)

8. A circular piece of metal expands by heat so that the radius increases at the rate of 0.01 inch per second. At what rate is the surface increasing when the radius is 2 inches?

9. Gas is escaping from a spherical balloon at the rate of 900 cubic inches per minute. At what rate is the radius decreasing, when the radius is 9 inches?

10. A train moves along the parabolic curve $y = 3x^2 - 2x$. If the rate with respect to the x-axis is 6 miles per hour, what is the rate of the train with respect to the y-axis, when $x = 2$?

11

INTEGRATION

11-1 Integration as Anti-differentiation

Integration is the inverse operation of differentiation. Some inverse operations are familiar to the student. For example, subtraction is the inverse of addition, division is the inverse of multiplication, extracting a root is the inverse of raising to a power. Likewise, integration is the inverse operation of differentiation. Here, the operation is that of finding the original function from which the derivative was found; i.e., if $f'(x)$ is known, what is $f(x)$?

11-2 Constant of Integration

As an example, let it be required to find the equation of a curve whose slope at any point is equal to twice the abscissa of that point.

Thus, $$\frac{dy}{dx} = 2x.$$

From the student's experience with differentiation, it is seen that $y = x^2$ is a function such that its derivative is

$$\frac{dy}{dx} = 2x.$$

However, $y = x^2 + 7$, $y = x^2 - 3$, $y = x^2 - \frac{2}{3}$, etc., are also functions such that their derivatives are $\frac{dy}{dx} = 2x$, since the derivative of a constant is always zero.

Hence, if
$$\frac{dy}{dx} = 2x,$$

then
$$y = x^2 + C,$$

where C is any constant is the *family* of curves whose derivative

$$\frac{dy}{dx} = 2x.$$

Thus, it is seen that, although for each single-valued function there is only *one* derivative, for each derivative there is an *infinity* of functions.

If an additional condition is given, such as that the curve passes through the point (2,9), then it is seen that only *one* of the curves of the family $y = x^2 + C$ passes through the point (2,9).

The constant C can then be found. For, by substituting the coordinates of the point in the equation,

$$9 = 4 + C$$
and
$$C = 5.$$

Therefore, if $\frac{dy}{dx} = 2x$ and the curve passes through the point (2,9), the equation of the curve is

$$y = x^2 + 5.$$

In Fig. 11-1, the curves (a) $y = x^2 + 5$, (b) $y = x^2$, and (c) $y = x^2 - 3$ are sketched.

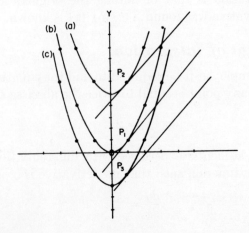

Fig. 11-1.

At the point P_1 on the curve $y = x^2$, where $x = 1$, the slope of the tangent to the curve is $\frac{dy}{dx} = 2x = 2(1) = 2$. Likewise, at the point P_2 on curve $y = x^2 + 5$ and the point P_3 on the curve $y = x^2 - 3$, where $x = 1$, the slopes of the tangents are also 2.

Therefore, for any point on the curves $y = x^2 + C$ where $x = 1$ the slope of the tangent is 2.

11-3 The Symbol of Integration

If $\frac{dy}{dx} = f'(x)$ and it is required to find $f(x)$, the operation is indicated by writing

$$\int f'(x) \, dx = f(x) + C,$$

where the symbol "$\int$" is called the "integral sign" and the equation is read "the integral of $f'(x)$ is $f(x)$ plus C."

The integral sign "$\int$" and the symbol "dx" are really one symbol, where the integral sign "$\int$" indicates the operation of integration and the "dx" indicates that x is the variable of integration.

Hence, the entire symbol $\int \ldots dx$ represents the inverse operation to that which is represented by the symbol $\frac{d}{dx} \ldots$.

11-4 Power Formula for Integration

Since
$$\frac{d}{dx}(4x^2 + 6) = 8x,$$

then
$$\int 8x \, dx = 4x^2 + C.$$

And, since
$$\frac{d}{dx}(3x^{\frac{1}{2}}) = \frac{3}{2} x^{-\frac{1}{2}},$$

then
$$\int \frac{3}{2} x^{-\frac{1}{2}} \, dx = 3x^{\frac{1}{2}} + C.$$

The above numerical examples show that, in finding the derivative of the power function of x, the coefficient is multiplied by the exponent and the power is reduced by 1. So, in finding the integral of a power function, the power of x is increased by 1 and the coefficient is divided by this number.

Thus, follows the power formula of integration,

$$\int ax^n \, dx = \frac{a}{n+1} x^{n+1} + C \quad (\text{where } n \neq -1).$$

Frequently, it is more convenient to place the constant in front of the integral sign, as

$$a \int x^n \, dx = \frac{a}{n+1} x^{n+1} + C \quad (\text{where } n \neq -1).$$

EXAMPLE 1. Find $\int 8x^3 \, dx$.

$$8 \int x^3 \, dx = 8(\tfrac{1}{4})x^4 + C$$
$$= 2x^4 + C.$$

Since integration is the inverse operation of differentiation, all results should be checked by differentiation.

Thus, $\qquad\qquad \dfrac{d}{dx}(2x^4 + C) = 8x^3.$

EXAMPLE 2. Find $\int 6x^{-\frac{1}{2}} \, dx$.

$$6 \int x^{-\frac{1}{2}} \, dx = \frac{6}{\frac{1}{2}} x^{\frac{1}{2}} + C$$
$$= 12x^{\frac{1}{2}} + C.$$

EXAMPLE 3. Find $y = \int \dfrac{2}{x^3} \, dx$.

$$y = 2 \int x^{-3} \, dx$$
$$= 2(-\tfrac{1}{2})x^{-2} + C$$
$$= -\frac{1}{x^2} + C.$$

E X E R C I S E S

Find the following integrals and check by differentiation.

1. $\int 6x^2 \, dx.$

2. $\int 6x^{\frac{4}{5}} \, dx.$

3. $\int 2x^3 \, dx.$

4. $\int 6x\sqrt{x} \, dx.$

5. $\displaystyle\int 4\sqrt{x}\,dx.$

6. $\displaystyle\int gt\,dt.$

7. $\displaystyle\int 6\sqrt[3]{x^2}\,dx.$

8. $\displaystyle\int 4at^3\,dt.$

9. $\displaystyle\int \frac{10}{x^3}\,dx.$

10. $\displaystyle\frac{\pi}{16}\int x^3\,dx.$

11. Find the equation of the curve whose slope at any point is $3x^2$ and which passes through the point (1,2).

12. Find the equation of the curve whose slope at any point is $4x$ and which passes through the point (2,5).

13. Find the equation of the curve whose slope at any point is equal to the square of the abscissa at that point and which passes through the point (2,3).

11-5 Integration of Sum of Functions

Let $\displaystyle\frac{dy}{dx} = f_1(x) + f_2(x) + \ldots + f_n(x).$

Then $\displaystyle y = \int [f_1(x) + f_2(x) + \ldots + f_n(x)]\,dx.$

Since the derivative of the algebraic sum of any number of functions is equal to the same algebraic sum of their derivatives, and since integration is the inverse operation of differentiation, it follows that,

if $\displaystyle y = \int [f_1(x) + f_2(x) + \ldots + f_n(x)]\,dx,$

then $\displaystyle y = \int f_1(x)\,dx + \int f_2(x)\,dx + \ldots + \int f_n(x)\,dx.$

Hence, the integral of the algebraic sum of any number of functions is equal to the same algebraic sum of the integrals.

EXAMPLE 1. Find the integral $\displaystyle y = \int (2x^3 - 5x^2 - 3x + 4)\,dx.$

Then $\displaystyle y = \int 2x^3\,dx - \int 5x^2\,dx - \int 3x\,dx + \int 4\,dx.$

Therefore,
$$y = \frac{x^4}{2} - \frac{5x^3}{3} - \frac{3x^2}{2} + 4x + C.$$

EXAMPLE 2. Find the integral $y = \int (7 - x)^2 \, dx$.

$$y = \int (49 - 56x + 16x^2) \, dx$$
$$= 49x - 28x^2 + \tfrac{16}{3}x^3 + C.$$

EXAMPLE 3. Given $f'(x) = 3x^2 - 5x - 1$ and that the curve passes through the point (4,7), find the equation of the curve.

$$f'(x) = 3x^2 - 5x - 1.$$
$$f(x) = \int (3x^2 - 5x - 1) \, dx$$
$$= x^3 - \tfrac{5}{2}x^2 - x + C.$$

To find C, substitute (4,7) in $f(x)$:

$$7 = 64 - 40 - 4 + C,$$
$$C = -13.$$

Therefore, $\qquad f(x) = x^3 - \tfrac{5}{2}x^2 - x - 13.$

E X E R C I S E S

Find the following integrals:

1. $\int (3x^2 + 2x - 6) \, dx.$

2. $\int (ax + b) \, dx.$

3. $\int (3x^2 - 2x^{\frac{1}{2}} + 5) \, dx.$

4. $\int (10x^{-2} - 2x^{-3} - \tfrac{4}{5}x^{-5}) \, dx.$

5. $\int \frac{(4 - 3x^2)}{6} \, dx.$

6. $\int (a - t)^3 \, dt.$

7. $\int (3x^{-2} - x - 2 + 10x^{\frac{2}{3}}) \, dx.$

8. $\int (2x^{-\frac{1}{3}} + 6) \, dx.$

9. $\int \frac{2x^2 - 5}{x^2} \, dx.$

10. $\int \left(\dfrac{2}{\sqrt{x}} + \dfrac{1}{4}\sqrt{x} - 2\sqrt[3]{x} \right) dx.$

In each of the following integrals find the original function so that it passes through the indicated point:

11. $y = \int (x - 2)\, dx;\ (9,20).$

12. $y = \int (3x^2 - 4)\, dx;\ (1,-5).$

13. $y = \int (x + 2x^{-2} - 3x^{-3})\, dx;\ (-1,0).$

14. Find the equation of the curve whose slope at any point is $2x - 3$ and which passes through the point $(-1,5)$.

15. Find the equation of the curve whose slope at any point is equal to the negative reciprocal of the square of the abscissa at that point and which passes through the point $(1,1)$.

11-6 Integrals Involving u^n, Where $u = f(x)$

The procedure for carrying out such integrations is best illustrated by the following examples:

EXAMPLE 1. Find the integral $y = \int \sqrt{2 - 3x}\, dx.$

By inspection, it is seen that $(2 - 3x)^{\frac{1}{2}}$, multiplied by some constant, is the derivative of the function $(2 - 3x)^{\frac{3}{2}}$.

Since $\quad \dfrac{d}{dx}(2 - 3x)^{\frac{3}{2}} = \dfrac{3}{2}(2 - 3x)^{\frac{1}{2}}(-3),$

the factors $\frac{3}{2}$ and -3 must be introduced after the integral sign. Thus the quantity under the integral sign becomes an *exact* derivative. To compensate, the reciprocal factors, $\frac{2}{3}$ and $-\frac{1}{3}$ must be placed in front of the integral sign.

Thus, $\quad y = (\tfrac{2}{3})(-\tfrac{1}{3}) \int (\tfrac{3}{2})(2 - 3x)^{\frac{1}{2}}(-3)\, dx.$

Therefore, $\quad y = -\tfrac{2}{9}(2 - 3x)^{\frac{3}{2}} + C.$

This result can be verified by differentiation.

EXAMPLE 2. Find the integral $y = \int \dfrac{x\, dx}{\sqrt{2x^2 - 3}}.$

$$y = \int x(2x^2 - 3)^{-\frac{1}{2}}\, dx.$$

Since $x(2x^2-3)^{-\frac{1}{2}}$ multiplied by a constant is the derivative of $(2x^2 - 3)^{\frac{1}{2}}$, the quantity under the integral sign can be made an *exact* derivative of $(2x^2 - 3)^{\frac{1}{2}}$, as follows:

$$y = (2) \int (\tfrac{1}{2})(2x^2 - 3)^{-\frac{1}{2}}(x) \, dx$$

$$= (\tfrac{1}{4})(2) \int (\tfrac{1}{2})(2x^2 - 3)^{-\frac{1}{2}}(4x) \, dx.$$

Therefore, $\quad y = \frac{1}{2}(2x^2 - 3)^{\frac{1}{2}} + C.$

EXAMPLE 3. Find the integral $y = \int x(3 - x^2)^{\frac{2}{3}} \, dx.$

$$y = (-\tfrac{1}{2})(\tfrac{3}{5}) \int (\tfrac{5}{3})(3 - x^2)^{\frac{2}{3}}(-2x) \, dx.$$

Therefore, $\quad y = -\frac{3}{10}(3 - x^2)^{\frac{5}{3}} + C.$

E X E R C I S E S

Integrate the following and check by differentiation:

1. $\int \sqrt{2x + 1} \, dx.$

2. $\int (x - 1)^{\frac{1}{3}} \, dx.$

3. $\int \sqrt{4 - 3x} \, dx.$

4. $\int x(2 + x^2) \, dx.$

5. $\int x\sqrt{x^2 - 1} \, dx.$

6. $\int x(x^2 - 3)^2 \, dx.$

7. $\int x\sqrt{4 - x^2} \, dx.$

8. $\int x^2(2x^3 - 5)^2 \, dx.$

9. $\int (3x - 5)^{\frac{3}{2}} \, dx.$

10. $\int 2t^2(5 - 3t^3) \, dt.$

11. $\int \dfrac{dx}{\sqrt{5 - 3x}}.$

12. $\int \dfrac{dt}{(2 - at)^3}.$

13. $\int \dfrac{x \, dx}{\sqrt{x^2 + 4}}.$

14. $\int \dfrac{x \, dx}{\sqrt{5 - x^2}}.$

15. $\int 4x\sqrt{1 - 3x^2} \, dx.$

16. $\int (a + bx)^{\frac{1}{2}} \, dx.$

17. $\int v\sqrt{a^2 + v^2} \, dv.$

18. $\int x\sqrt{a^2 + b^2x^2} \, dx.$

11-7 The Definite Integral—Area Under a Curve

An important application of the anti-derivative (i.e., the integral) is that of finding the area under a given curve.

Let $DQRB$ (Fig. 11-2) be the curve which the function $y = f(x)$ represents.

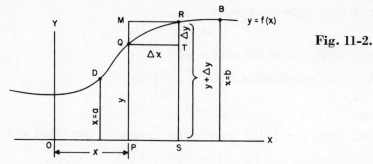

Fig. 11-2.

Further, let $DQRB$ be continuous between the lines $x = a$ and $x = b$ and lie entirely *above* the x-axis.

The problem is to find the area A bounded by the curve $y = f(x)$, the x-axis, and the ordinates $x = a$ and $x = b$.

This area can be considered as generated by a moving ordinate starting from $x = a$ and sweeping out the required area A after reaching $x = b$.

On moving from the position PQ to the position SR an increment of area $PQRS$ is swept out (Fig. 11-2). Denote this increment of area ΔA. The area of rectangle $PQTS = y\,\overline{\Delta x}$ and the area of rectangle $PMRS = (y + \Delta y)\,\overline{\Delta x}$.

By taking Δx sufficiently small, the curve is either ascending or descending at all points between Q and R.

Therefore, $\qquad y\,\overline{\Delta x} < \overline{\Delta A} < (y + \overline{\Delta y})\,\overline{\Delta x}.$

Divide both sides by Δx:

$$y < \frac{\Delta A}{\Delta x} < (y + \Delta y).$$

Therefore, $\quad \dfrac{\Delta A}{\Delta x}$ lies between y and $(y + \Delta y)$.

Then, as $\Delta x \to 0$,

$\Delta y \to 0$ and $\displaystyle\lim_{\Delta x \to 0} \frac{\Delta A}{\Delta x}$ lies between y and $\displaystyle\lim_{\Delta y \to 0}(y + \Delta y).$

Hence, $\qquad \displaystyle\lim_{\Delta x \to 0} \frac{\Delta A}{\Delta x} = y$

and
$$\frac{dA}{dx} = y.$$

Consequently, $\qquad A = \int y \, dx = \int f(x) \, dx.$

Now, let $F(x)$ be a function whose derivative is $f(x)$.
Therefore upon integrating,
$$A = F(x) + C.$$

But, when $x = a$, the area is zero.

Then, by substituting, $\quad 0 = F(a) + C$
and $\qquad\qquad\qquad\quad C = -F(a),$
and $\qquad\qquad\qquad\quad A = F(x) - F(a).$

But, when $x = b$, the required area has been generated and
$$A = F(b) - F(a).$$

This difference is represented by the symbol
$$\int_a^b y \, dx \quad \text{or} \quad \int_a^b f(x) \, dx,$$
and is read, "the integral of $F(x)$ in the interval from a to b."

In summary, the area under the curve $y = f(x)$ from a to b is equal to
$$\int_a^b f(x) \, dx = \Big[F(x) \Big]_a^b = F(b) - F(a),$$
where $F(x)$ is the anti-derivative of $f(x)$ and the standard notation $\Big[F(x) \Big]_a^b$ means: first replace x by the upper value, b, to find $F(b)$ and from this subtract $F(a)$ which is obtained by replacing x by the lower value, a, in $F(x)$.

Since the integral $\int_a^b f(x) \, dx$ has a definite numerical value, it is called a *definite integral*.

It may be noted that the constant of integration disappears in the subtraction, for, if
$$\int f(x) \, dx = F(x) + C,$$
then $\qquad \int_a^b f(x) \, dx = \Big[F(x) + C \Big]_a^b$
$$= [F(b) + C] - [F(a) + C]$$
$$= F(b) - F(a).$$

This method of finding the area under a curve is applicable only if (a) the curve is continuous in the interval from a to b, and (b) the curve is above the x-axis in the interval from a to b.

EXAMPLE 1. Evaluate the definite integral $\int_2^4 \left(x + \dfrac{1}{x^2} \right) dx.$

$$\int_2^4 (x + x^{-2}) \, dx = \left[\tfrac{1}{2}x^2 - x^{-1} \right]_2^4$$
$$= (8 - \tfrac{1}{4}) - (2 - \tfrac{1}{2})$$
$$= \tfrac{31}{4} - \tfrac{3}{2} = \tfrac{25}{4}.$$

EXAMPLE 2. Find the area bounded by the parabola $y = x^2$, the x-axis, and the lines $x = 2$ and $x = 4$ (Fig. 11-3).

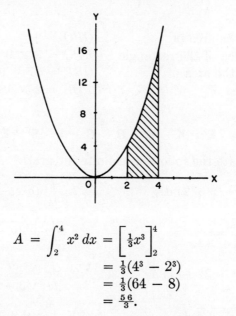

Fig. 11-3.

$$A = \int_2^4 x^2 \, dx = \left[\tfrac{1}{3}x^3 \right]_2^4$$
$$= \tfrac{1}{3}(4^3 - 2^3)$$
$$= \tfrac{1}{3}(64 - 8)$$
$$= \tfrac{56}{3}.$$

EXAMPLE 3. Find the area inside the parabola $y = x^2$ to the depth of 9 units.

Since $y = 9$ (Fig. 11-4), then, by substitution in $y = x^2$, $9 = x^2$ and $x = \pm 3$. Therefore, the points $S(-3,9)$ and $P(3,9)$ are points on the curve.

To find the area of $SRPOS$, it is first necessary to find the area of OPQ by the definite integral

$$\int_0^3 x^2 \, dx = \left[\tfrac{1}{3}x^3 \right]_0^3$$
$$= \tfrac{1}{3}(27 - 0) = 9.$$

Integration / 143

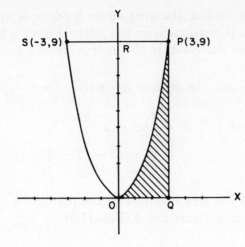

Fig. 11-4.

S(-3,9)   P(3,9)

Therefore the area of $OPQ = 9.$
But, the area of the rectangle $ORPQ = 3 \times 9 = 27.$
Therefore, the area of $ORP = 27 - 9 = 18,$
and the area of $SRPOS = 2 \times 18 = 36.$

E X E R C I S E S

Evaluate the following definite integrals:

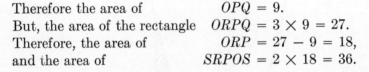

1. $\int_0^5 (x^2 - x + 2)\, dx.$

7. $\int_0^a (a^2x - x^3)\, dx.$

2. $\int_1^6 \dfrac{dx}{\sqrt{x+3}}.$

8. $\int_1^5 \sqrt{2t - 1}\, dt.$

3. $\int_0^3 (2x^2 - 3x - 1)\, dx.$

9. $\int_0^1 \dfrac{dt}{\sqrt{3 - 2t}}.$

4. $\int_0^3 x\sqrt{x^2 + 4}\, dx.$

10. $\int_{-1}^1 (x + 1)^2\, dx.$

5. $\int_1^8 (\sqrt{x} + \sqrt[3]{x})\, dx.$

11. $\int_2^5 \dfrac{dt}{\sqrt{6 - t}}.$

6. $\int_0^3 \dfrac{x\, dx}{\sqrt{x^2 + 16}}.$

12. $\int_0^2 \dfrac{x^2 + 1}{x^2}\, dx.$

13. Find the area bounded by the cubical parabola $2y = x^3$, the x-axis, and the line $x = 4$.

14. Find the area bounded by the cubical parabola $2y = x^3$, the y-axis, and the line $y = 32$.

15. Find the area bounded by the cubical parabola $y = x^3 + 3$, the y-axis, the x-axis, and the line $x = 4$.

16. Find the area bounded by the parabola $y = x^2$ and the line $y = 2x$.

17. Find the area bounded by the semi-cubical parabola $x^2 = y^3$, the y-axis, and the line $y = 4$.

18. Find the area bounded by the parabola $y = 9 - x^2$, the x-axis, and the lines $x = 0$ and $x = 3$.

19. Find the area bounded by the parabola $y = 3x^2 + 4x + 1$, the x-axis, and the lines $x = 2$ and $x = 4$.

20. Find the area enclosed by the parabola $y = 3x - \frac{3}{4}x^2$ and the x-axis.

APPENDIX

Formulas from Elementary Mathematics

ALGEBRA

1. Laws of Exponents

$$a^p \cdot a^q = a^{p+q}, \quad a \neq 0$$
$$a^p \div a^q = a^{p-q},$$
$$a^0 = 1,$$
$$a^{-p} = \frac{1}{a^p},$$
$$(a^p)^q = a^{pq},$$
$$a^{\frac{p}{q}} = \sqrt[q]{a^p}.$$

2. Factorial Numbers

$$n! = n(n-1)(n-2)\cdots 2 \cdot 1.$$

3. Binomial Theorem

For n a positive integer,

$$(a+b)^n = a^n + na^{n-1}b + \frac{n(n-1)}{2!}\, a^{n-2}b^2$$

$$+ \frac{n(n-1)(n-2)}{3!}\, a^{n-3}b^3 + \cdots + nab^{n-1} + b^n.$$

4. The Quadratic Formula

The roots of $ax^2 + bx + c = 0$, where $a \neq 0$, are given by the formula

$$x = \frac{-b \pm \sqrt{b^2 - 4ac}}{2a}.$$

TRIGONOMETRY

1. Definitions of Functions

$$\sin \theta = \frac{y}{r} = \frac{1}{\csc \theta},$$

$$\cos \theta = \frac{x}{r} = \frac{1}{\sec \theta},$$

$$\tan \theta = \frac{y}{x} = \frac{1}{\cot \theta},$$

$$\cot \theta = \frac{x}{y} = \frac{1}{\tan \theta}.$$

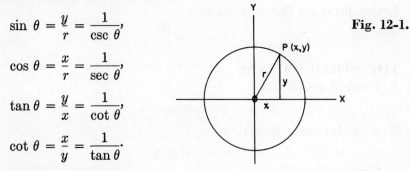

Fig. 12-1.

2. Fundamental Relations

$$\sin^2 \theta + \cos^2 \theta = 1,$$

$$\tan (90° + \theta) = -\cot \theta = -\frac{1}{\tan \theta}.$$

3. Circular Measure of Angles

The unit of circular measure is a radian, which is the central angle subtended by an arc equal to the radius of the circle.

Here, $\qquad\qquad 180° = \pi \qquad$ (when no unit is indicated, radian is understood),

$$1 \text{ radian} = \frac{180°}{\pi},$$

$$1° = \frac{\pi}{180}.$$

Therefore, $\qquad\qquad 90° = \frac{\pi}{2},$

$$30° = \frac{\pi}{6}, \quad \text{etc.}$$

Formulas from Analytic Geometry

FORMULAS OF DISTANCE AND DIRECTION

1. Distance

$$d = \sqrt{(x_1 - x_2)^2 + (y_1 - y_2)^2}.$$

2. Midpoint

$$x_0 = \tfrac{1}{2}(x_1 + x_2); \quad y_0 = \tfrac{1}{2}(y_1 + y_2).$$

3. Slope

$$m = \frac{y_1 - y_2}{x_1 - x_2}.$$

4. Condition for Parallelism

$$m_1 = m_2.$$

5. Condition for Perpendicularity

$$m_1 = -\frac{1}{m_2}.$$

THE STRAIGHT LINE

1. Point-Slope Equation

$$y - y_1 = m(x - x_1).$$

2. Slope-Intercept Equation

$$y = mx + b.$$

3. General Equation

$$Ax + By + C = 0.$$

4. Distance from point (x_1, y_1) to line $Ax + By + C = 0$

$$d = \left| \frac{Ax_1 + By_1 + C}{\sqrt{A^2 + B^2}} \right|.$$

THE CIRCLE

1. Center at (h,k)

$$(x - h)^2 + (y - k)^2 = r^2.$$

2. Center at Origin

$$x^2 + y^2 = r^2.$$

3. General Form

$$Ax^2 + Ay^2 + Dx + Ey + F = 0.$$

THE ELLIPSE

1. Center at Origin

$$\frac{x^2}{a^2} + \frac{y^2}{b^2} = 1 \quad \text{or} \quad \frac{x^2}{b^2} + \frac{y^2}{a^2} = 1.$$

2. Center at (h,k)

$$\frac{(x - h)^2}{a^2} + \frac{(y - k)^2}{b^2} = 1 \quad \text{or} \quad \frac{(x - h)^2}{b^2} + \frac{(y - k)^2}{a^2} = 1.$$

3. Relationship of the Constants

$$a > b; \quad a^2 = b^2 + c^2.$$

THE PARABOLA
1. Vertex at Origin
$$x^2 = 4py \quad \text{or} \quad y^2 = 4px.$$
2. Vertex at (h,k)
$$(x - h)^2 = 4p(y - k) \quad \text{or} \quad (y - k)^2 = 4p(x - h).$$

THE HYPERBOLA
1. Center at Origin
$$\frac{x^2}{a^2} - \frac{y^2}{b^2} = 1 \quad \text{or} \quad \frac{x^2}{b^2} - \frac{y^2}{a^2} = 1.$$
2. Center at (h,k)
$$\frac{(x - h)^2}{a^2} - \frac{(y - k)^2}{b^2} = 1 \quad \text{or} \quad \frac{(x - h)^2}{b^2} - \frac{(y - k)^2}{a^2} = 1.$$
3. Relationship of the Constants
$$c > a, \quad c^2 = a^2 + b^2.$$
4. Equilateral Hyperbolas
$$\frac{x^2}{a^2} - \frac{y^2}{a^2} = 1,$$

$$xy = k.$$

POLAR COORDINATES
1. Relation to Rectangular Coordinates
$$x = \rho \cos \theta, \qquad y = \rho \sin \theta;$$
$$\rho = \sqrt{x^2 + y^2}, \quad \theta = \text{arc tan} \frac{y}{x}.$$

Differentiation of Algebraic Functions

1. $\dfrac{d(ax^n)}{dx} = nax^{n-1}.$

2. $\dfrac{d(c)}{dx} = 0.$

3. $\dfrac{d(au^n)}{dx} = nau^{n-1} \dfrac{du}{dx}$ [where $u = f(x)$].

4. $\dfrac{d(u + v + w)}{dx} = \dfrac{du}{dx} + \dfrac{dv}{dx} + \dfrac{dw}{dx}.$

5. $\dfrac{d(uv)}{dx} = u \cdot \dfrac{dv}{dx} + v \cdot \dfrac{du}{dx}.$

6. $\dfrac{d\left(\dfrac{u}{v}\right)}{dx} = \dfrac{v \cdot \dfrac{du}{dx} - u \cdot \dfrac{dv}{dx}}{v^2}.$

ANSWERS TO EXERCISES

(Answers are given to the odd-numbered exercises, except where the exercises are construction problems, where the answers are obvious, or where the giving of the answers will destroy the usefulness of the exercises.)

Pages 3, 4, 5

1. -3; -2; 2; -5; $x-4$ 5. -1; 2; $\frac{2}{3}$; -3; $\dfrac{1+x}{1-x}$

3. 21; 9; 13; 5; 6 7. 1; 0; $1+\frac{1}{2}\sqrt{2}$; -1; 0

9. All real numbers, $y \geq 1$;
    $x \geq 0$, all real numbers except $y = 0$;
    All real numbers except $x = 1$, all real numbers except $y = 1$;
    $|x| \geq 4$, $y \geq 0$

11. $3 \leq x \leq 5$;
    All real numbers except $x = 0$ and $x = -1$;
    All real numbers except $-1 < x \leq 0$;
    $|x| > \sqrt{2}$, all real numbers

Page 10

5. A square

Page 13

1. -5 3. -8 5. 8 7. -7 9. $-b$

Pages 15, 16

1. 5
3. 5
5. $8\sqrt{2}$

7. 10
9. 5
11. 17

13. $5\sqrt{a^2 + b^2}$
21. Isosceles
23. 1

Page 18

1. (6,2)
3. (−3,−4)
5. $(-\frac{7}{2}, \frac{3}{2})$

7. (−2,−7)
9. (6,7)
11. $(\frac{5}{2}, \frac{19}{2})$

13. (0,4), (1,7), (4,5)
15. (0,4); 5

Page 23

1. $-\frac{3}{2}$

3. $-\frac{1}{5}$

5. 0

Pages 25, 26

1. $2x - y + 1 = 0$
3. $2x + y - 10 = 0$
5. $2x + 3y + 9 = 0$
7. $2x + 5y + 4 = 0$
9. $7x + 9y = 0$

11. $4x - 3y - 11 = 0$
13. $x - y - 5 = 0$
15. $3x - 2y - 1 = 0$
17. $x + y - 4 = 0$
19. $5x - 7y - 35 = 0$

Page 27

1. $3x - y - 5 = 0$
3. $x + 7 = 0$

5. $x + y + 7 = 0$

Page 28

1. $x - 3y = 0$
3. $3x + y = 0$

5. $2x - 7y = 0$

Page 29

1. $y + 3 = 0$
3. $x + 5 = 0$

5. $x - 3 = 0$

Page 32

1. Perpendicular
3. Perpendicular
5. Perpendicular
7. Parallel

9. $3x + 2y + 11 = 0$
11. $5x - y + 8 = 0$
13. $2x + 7y - 47 = 0$

Pages 34, 35

1. $\frac{8}{5}$
3. 6

5. $\frac{11}{5}$
7. 1

9. $\frac{29}{6}\sqrt{2}$
11. $\frac{27}{13}\sqrt{13}$

15. $\frac{21}{5}$

Pages 38, 39

1. $x^2 + y^2 - 25 = 0$
3. $x^2 + y^2 - 16 = 0$

5. $x^2 + y^2 - 4x - 8y - 5 = 0$
7. $x^2 + y^2 - 18x + 6y + 81 = 0$
9. $4x^2 + 4y^2 - 24x - 4y - 107 = 0$
11. $16x^2 + 16y^2 - 56x + 144y + 369 = 0$
13. $x^2 + y^2 + 4x - 4y - 17 = 0$

Pages 40, 41

1. Center $(4, -5)$; radius 6
3. Center $(2, -3)$; radius 7
5. Center $(-6, 5)$; radius 9
7. Center $(-5, 0)$; radius 5

9. Center $(0, 4)$; radius 5
11. Center $(-\frac{3}{2}, -2)$; radius $\frac{5}{2}$
13. Center $(\frac{2}{3}, -\frac{5}{3})$; radius $\frac{5}{3}\sqrt{2}$

Page 42

1. $x^2 + y^2 - 8x = 0$
3. $x^2 + y^2 - 14x + 8y + 40 = 0$
5. $x^2 + y^2 - 2x + 4y - 3 = 0$

7. $x^2 + y^2 + 4x - 21 = 0$
9. $x^2 + y^2 + 2x - 2y - 23 = 0$

Pages 45, 46

1. Axes, 5, 4; foci $(\pm 3, 0)$; e $= \frac{3}{5}$
3. Axes, 3, 2; foci $(\pm \sqrt{5}, 0)$; e $= \dfrac{\sqrt{5}}{3}$
5. Axes, 5, 3; foci $(\pm 4, 0)$; e $= \frac{4}{5}$
7. Axes, $\sqrt{6}$, 2; foci $(\pm \sqrt{2}, 0)$; e $= \frac{1}{3}\sqrt{3}$
9. Axes, 8, 5; foci $(\pm \sqrt{39}, 0)$; e $= \frac{1}{8}\sqrt{39}$
11. Axes, $\sqrt{3}$, $\frac{3}{2}$; foci $(\pm\frac{1}{2}\sqrt{3}, 0)$; e $= \frac{1}{2}$
13. $9x^2 + 25y^2 - 225 = 0$
15. $9x^2 + 25y^2 - 225 = 0$
17. $3x^2 + 4y^2 - 432 = 0$

Page 47

1. $a = 5$, $b = 3$; F: $(0, \pm 4)$; e $= \frac{4}{5}$
3. $a = 6$, $b = 2$; F: $(0, \pm 4\sqrt{2})$; e $= \frac{2}{3}\sqrt{2}$
5. $a = 9$, $b = 3\sqrt{3}$; F: $(0, \pm 3\sqrt{6})$; e $= \frac{1}{3}\sqrt{6}$
7. $a = 2\sqrt{5}$, $b = 2$; F: $(0, \pm 4)$; e $= \frac{2}{5}\sqrt{5}$

Page 49

1. C: $(2, -1)$; F: $(-2, -1)$ and $(6, -1)$; $a = 5$, $b = 3$; e $= \frac{4}{5}$.
3. C: $(1, -2)$; F: $(1 \pm \sqrt{7}, -2)$; $a = 4$, $b = 3$; e $= \frac{1}{4}\sqrt{7}$
5. C: $(0, 2)$; F: $(\pm 4, 2)$; $a = 5$, $b = 3$; e $= \frac{4}{5}$
7. C: $(-2, 3)$; F: $(-2, 3 \pm 4\sqrt{3})$; $a = 8$, $b = 4$; e $= \frac{1}{2}\sqrt{3}$
9. C: $(0, 3)$; F: $(\pm 2\sqrt{2}, 3)$; $a = 3$, $b = 1$; e $= \frac{2}{3}\sqrt{2}$
11. C: $(\frac{3}{2}, -\frac{1}{2})$; F: $(\frac{3}{2} \pm 2\sqrt{2}, -\frac{1}{2})$; $a = 3$, $b = 1$; e $= \frac{2}{3}\sqrt{2}$

Page 52

11. $y^2 = 8x$

13. $y^2 = -4x$

15. $x^2 = 64y; y^2 = \frac{1}{8}x$

Page 54

15. $x^2 - 6x - 8y + 9 = 0$

17. $y^2 - 4x + 2y - 3 = 0$

Pages 58, 59

1. $a = 3$; F: $(\pm\sqrt{10},0)$; e $= \frac{1}{3}\sqrt{10}$; A: $x \pm 3y = 0$

3. $a = 3$; F: $(\pm\sqrt{13},0)$; e $= \frac{1}{3}\sqrt{13}$; A: $2x \pm 3y = 0$

5. $a = 4$; F: $(0,\pm2\sqrt{13})$; e $= \frac{1}{2}\sqrt{13}$; A: $2x \pm 3y = 0$

7. $a = 3$; F: $(\pm\sqrt{34},0)$; e $= \frac{1}{3}\sqrt{34}$; A: $5x \pm 3y = 0$

9. $a = 10$; F: $(0,\pm5\sqrt{5})$; e $= \frac{1}{2}\sqrt{5}$; A: $2x \pm y = 0$

11. $a = 4$; F: $(0,\pm4\sqrt{2}$; e $= \sqrt{2}$; A: $x \pm y = 0$

13. $a = \frac{1}{2}\sqrt{10}$; F: $(\pm\frac{5}{6}\sqrt{6},0)$; e $= \frac{1}{3}\sqrt{15}$; A: $\sqrt{6}x \pm 3y = 0$

15. $3x^2 - y^2 - 12 = 0$

17. $16x^2 - 9y^2 + 144 = 0$

19. $x^2 - y^2 - 1 = 0$

Page 62

1. $(2,2)$; $(-2,-2)$

3. $(4,4)$; $(-4,-4)$

5. $(\sqrt{10},\sqrt{10})$; $(-\sqrt{10},-\sqrt{10})$

7. $(10,10)$; $(-10,-10)$

11. $(3,-2)$; $(1,-4)$, $(5,0)$

13. $(-2,3)$; $(0,5)$, $(-4,1)$

Pages 63, 64

1. C: $(4,2)$; F: $(4 \pm \sqrt{13},2)$; $a = 3$; e $= \frac{1}{3}\sqrt{13}$; A: $2x - 3y - 2 = 0$ and $2x + 3y - 14 = 0$

3. C: $(-1,-2)$; F: $(-6,-2)$ and $(4,-2)$; $a = 4$; e $= \frac{5}{4}$; A: $3x - 4y - 5 = 0$ and $3x + 4y + 11 = 0$

5. C: $(-3,4)$; F: $(-3 \pm \sqrt{5}, 4)$; $a = 1$; e $= \sqrt{5}$; A: $2x - y + 10 = 0$ and $2x + y + 2 = 0$

7. C: $(2,0)$; F: $(2 \pm \sqrt{41},0)$; $a = 5$; e $= \frac{1}{5}\sqrt{41}$; A: $4x - 5y - 8 = 0$ and $4x + 5y - 8 = 0$

9. C: $(-\frac{3}{2},\frac{5}{2})$; F: $(-\frac{3}{2} \pm \frac{1}{2}\sqrt{13},\frac{5}{2})$; $a = \frac{3}{2}$; e $= \frac{1}{3}\sqrt{13}$; A: $4x - 6y + 21 = 0$ and $4x + 6y - 9 = 0$

Page 64

1. Parabola; $(y + 3)^2 = 8(x - 1)$

3. Ellipse; $\dfrac{(x + 3)^2}{4} + \dfrac{(y - 2)^2}{16} = 1$

5. Circle; $(x - 5)^2 + y^2 = 25$

7. Ellipse; $\dfrac{(x - 1)^2}{9} + \dfrac{(y + 2)^2}{18} = 1$

9. Parabola; $(x - 5)^2 = -8(y - 3)$

Pages 80, 81

1. $\left(\sqrt{2}, \dfrac{\pi}{4}\right)$

3. $\left(2, \dfrac{2\pi}{3}\right)$

5. $(1, \pi)$

7. $(\sqrt{2}, \sqrt{2})$

9. $(-1, 1)$

11. $(-3\sqrt{2}, 3\sqrt{2})$

13. $9x^2 - 16y^2 = 0$

15. $8x^2 + 9y^2 - 8x - 16 = 0$

17. $x^2 + y^2 - 8y = 0$

19. $\tan \theta = 4$

21. $\rho = 4$

23. $\rho^2 = \dfrac{36}{4 \cos^2 \theta - 9 \sin^2 \theta}$

Pages 88, 89

1. $x - y - 3 = 0$

3. $x^2 + y^2 + 8x = 0$

5. $4x - 2y - 3 = 0$

7. $25x^2 + 9y^2 - 225 = 0$

9. $16x^2 - 9y^2 - 144 = 0$

11. $x^2 + 2xy + y^2 - 16x - 8y + 40 = 0$

Page 95

1. 17

3. 2

5. 6

7. -2

9. 6

11. 6

Pages 101, 102

1. $6x$

3. $2x - 3$

5. $3x^2 - 5$

7. $-4x + 6; -2, 14$

9. $6x^2 - 3; -\tfrac{7}{3}, 3$

11. $6x^2 - 8x; 8, -\tfrac{5}{2}$

13. $-\dfrac{1}{x^2}; -1, -\tfrac{1}{4}$

15. $-\dfrac{4}{x^2}; -1, -1, -16$

Page 105

1. $10x$

3. -1

5. $-\tfrac{3}{2}x^{-\frac{3}{2}}$

7. $-x^{-\frac{1}{2}}$

9. $-32t$

11. $-4t^{\frac{1}{3}}$

Pages 106, 107

1. $6x - 4$

3. 4

5. $15x^2 - 7 + 6x^{-3}$

7. $2x^{-\frac{1}{2}} + \tfrac{3}{2}x^{-\frac{3}{2}}$

9. $3ax^2 - 6bx + 6c$

11. $3x^{\frac{1}{2}} - x^{-\frac{3}{4}} + x^{-\frac{3}{2}}$

13. 4, 4

15. 11, 92

17. $-2, 1$

19. 2

Page 109

1. $-18(2 - 3x)^2$

3. $\dfrac{2x}{\sqrt{x^2 + 1}}$

5. $-20x(x^2 - 3)^{-6}$

7. $2b(a + bx)$

9. $-\frac{1}{5}\sqrt{5}$

11. $\frac{4}{9}, 4$

13. $0, \dfrac{-4\pi r^2}{a}$

Page 111

1. $2(2 - 3x)(2 - 9x)$

3. $8x^3(x^2 + 2)(x^2 - 2)$

5. $\dfrac{2a + 3bx}{2\sqrt{a + bx}}$

7. $\dfrac{2x(3x^2 - 2)}{\sqrt{x^2 - 1}}$

9. $\dfrac{3(1 - 4x^2)}{\sqrt{1 - 2x^2}}$

11. $\dfrac{2x^3}{\sqrt{x^2 - 3}\,\sqrt{x^2 + 3}}$

13. $3x^2(x^3 + 1)^2(4x^3 + 1)$

15. $3, \frac{3}{4}\sqrt{6}$

17. $0, \frac{1}{2}$

Page 113

1. $\dfrac{1}{(1 - x)^2}$

3. $\dfrac{x^2 - 4x + 1}{(2 - x)^2}$

5. $\dfrac{4}{(2 + x)^2}$

7. $\dfrac{x^2 - 2x - 1}{(x - 1)^2}$

9. $\dfrac{3}{(1 - 3x)^2}$

11. $\dfrac{3ax^2 - a^3}{(2ax)^{\frac{3}{2}}}$

Page 114 (Review Exercises)

1. $-27(2 - 3x)^2$

3. $\dfrac{2x}{\sqrt{1 + x^2}}$

5. $2x + \dfrac{1}{x^2}$

7. $x^{-\frac{1}{2}} - x^{-\frac{2}{3}}$

9. $\dfrac{-ax}{b\sqrt{a^2 - x^2}}$

11. $\dfrac{-4x}{(x^2 - 1)^2}$

Pages 117, 118

1. Falling, critical, rising
3. Rising, critical, rising
5. Falling, critical, rising
7. Rising, rising, critical
9. Falling, rising

Page 120

1. Minimum at $(1,-4)$
3. Maximum at $(-4,70)$;
   minimum at $(2,-38)$
5. Maximum at $(-1,0)$;
   minimum at $(1,-4)$
7. Maximum at $(1,20)$;
   minimum at $(3,16)$

9. Maximum at $(\frac{5}{3},\frac{32}{27})$;
   minimum at $(3,0)$
11. Maximum at $(-2,21)$;
   minimum at $(2,-11)$
13. Maximum at $(-1,20)$;
   minimum at $(2,-7)$

Pages 127, 128

1. $b = 5$ in., $h = 5\sqrt{3}$ in.
3. 25 ft. by 25 ft. (a square);
   625 sq. ft.
5. 4
7. 16 and 16

9. $12\sqrt{2}$ in.
11. $b = 4\sqrt{3}$ in., $h = 4\sqrt{6}$ in.
13. $7\frac{1}{2}$ in. by 15 in. by 15 in.;
   $1687\frac{1}{2}$ cu. in.

Pages 131, 132

1. 195 ft. per sec; 25 ft. per sec;
   46 ft. per sec; 171 ft. per sec.
3. 1.6π cu. in. per sec.
5. $\dfrac{1}{8\pi}$ in. per sec.

7. $\frac{10}{9}\sqrt{14}$ ft. per sec.
9. $\dfrac{25}{9\pi}$ in. per sec.

Pages 136, 137

1. $2x^3 + C$
3. $\frac{1}{2}x^4 + C$
5. $\frac{8}{3}x^{\frac{3}{2}} + C$

7. $\frac{18}{5}x^{\frac{5}{3}} + C$
9. $-\dfrac{5}{x^2} + C$
11. $x^3 + 1$
13. $\frac{1}{3}x^3 + \frac{1}{3}$

Pages 138, 139

1. $x^3 + x^2 - 6x + C$
3. $x^3 - \frac{4}{3}x^{\frac{3}{2}} + 5x + C$
5. $\frac{2}{3}x - \frac{1}{6}x^3 + C$
7. $-3x^{-1} - \frac{1}{2}x^2 - 2x + 6x^{\frac{3}{3}} + C$

9. $2x + \dfrac{5}{x} + C$
11. $\frac{1}{2}x^2 - 2x - \frac{5}{2}$
13. $\frac{1}{2}x^2 - 2x^{-1} + \frac{3}{2}x^{-2} - 4$
15. $y = x^{-1}$

Page 140

1. $\frac{1}{3}(2x + 1)^{\frac{3}{2}} + C$
3. $-\frac{2}{9}(4 - 3x)^{\frac{3}{2}} + C$
5. $\frac{1}{3}(x^2 - 1)^{\frac{3}{2}} + C$
7. $-\frac{1}{3}(4 - x^2)^{\frac{3}{2}} + C$
9. $\frac{2}{15}(3x - 5)^{\frac{5}{2}} + C$

11. $-\frac{2}{3}(5 - 3x)^{\frac{1}{2}} + C$
13. $(x^2 + 4)^{\frac{1}{2}} + C$
15. $-\frac{4}{9}(1 - 3x^2)^{\frac{3}{2}} + C$
17. $\frac{1}{3}(a^2 + v^2)^{\frac{3}{2}} + C$

1. $\frac{235}{6}$

3. $\frac{3}{2}$

5. $\frac{32}{3}\sqrt{2} + \frac{127}{12}$

7. $\frac{1}{4}a^4$

9. $\sqrt{3} - 1$

11. 2

13. 32

15. 76

17. $\frac{64}{5}$

19. 82

INDEX

INDEX

Graphs (*Cont.*):
in polar coordinates, 85
in rectangular coordinates, 10, 11

───────── H ─────────

Hyperbola:
asymptotes of, 56
center of, 55
definition of, 54
eccentricity of, 54
equation of, 55, 62
foci of, 54
of form $xy = k$, 59
graph of, 57
principal axis of, 55
rectangular, 59
vertices of, 60
transverse axes of, 55
vertices of, 55

───────── I ─────────

Inclination of a straight line, 19
Increasing function, 115
Increments, 96
Independent variable, 1
Instantaneous rate of change, 129
Integrals, definite, 141
Integration:
of a^u where $u = f(x)$, 139
applications of, 141
constant of, 133
notations for, 135
power formula for, 135
of sum of functions, 137
Intercepts:
of a curve, 72
of a straight line, 11

───────── L ─────────

Leibnitz, Gottfried, 90
Length:
between two points, 14

Length (*Cont.*):
of line segment, 14
of line segment parallel to an axis, 12
Limits:
definition of, 91
of integration, 142
theorems on, 92
Line:
angle of inclination of, 19
distance from, to a point, 33
general equation of, 29
point-slope equation of, 24
polar equation of, 81
slope-intercept equation of, 24
slope of, 20
Line segment:
length of, 14
midpoint of, 16
Locus:
equation of, 86
of an equation, 86
problems, 86
Logarithmic equations, 69

───────── M ─────────

Major axis of an ellipse, 43
Maxima values of a function, 118
Midpoint of a line segment, 16
Minima values of a function, 118
Minor axis of an ellipse, 43

───────── N ─────────

Nature of the locus of a second-degree equation, 64
Newton, Sir Isaac, 90

───────── O ─────────

Ordinate, 7
Origin, 7

X

Y

3	4	5	6	7	8	9	10	11
60	61	62	63	64	65	66	67	68

Indeterminates

$$\frac{0}{0} \quad \frac{\infty}{\infty} \quad 0 \times \infty$$

$$\infty - \infty, \quad 0^0, \quad \infty^0, \quad 1^\infty$$

$$a^0 = 1$$

$$\frac{a}{\infty} = 0$$

$$\left(\frac{1}{a}\right)^\infty = 0$$